FOUR-FIGURE LOGARITHMS — *Continued*

N	0	1	2	3	4	5	6	7	8	9	1	2	3	4	5	6	7	8	9
55	7404	7412	7419	7427	7435	7443	7451	7459	7466	7474	1	2	2	3	4	5	5	6	7
56	7482	7490	7497	7505	7513	7520	7528	7536	7543	7551	1	2	2	3	4	5	5	6	7
57	7559	7566	7574	7582	7589	7597	7604	7612	7619	7627	1	2	2	3	4	5	5	6	7
58	7634	7642	7649	7657	7664	7672	7679	7686	7694	7701	1	1	2	3	4	4	5	6	7
59	7709	7716	7723	7731	7738	7745	7752	7760	7767	7774	1	1	2	3	4	4	5	6	7
60	7782	7789	7796	7803	7810	7818	7825	7832	7839	7846	1	1	2	3	4	4	5	6	6
61	7853	7860	7868	7875	7882	7889	7896	7903	7910	7917	1	1	2	3	4	4	5	6	6
62	7924	7931	7938	7945	7952	7959	7966	7973	7980	7987	1	1	2	3	3	4	5	6	6
63	7993	8000	8007	8014	8021	8028	8035	8041	8048	8055	1	1	2	3	3	4	5	5	6
64	8062	8069	8075	8082	8089	8096	8102	8109	8116	8122	1	1	2	3	3	4	5	5	6
65	8129	8136	8142	8149	8156	8162	8169	8176	8182	8189	1	1	2	3	3	4	5	5	6
66	8195	8202	8209	8215	8222	8228	8235	8241	8248	8254	1	1	2	3	3	4	5	5	6
67	8261	8267	8274	8280	8287	8293	8299	8306	8312	8319	1	1	2	3	3	4	5	5	6
68	8325	8331	8338	8344	8351	8357	8363	8370	8376	8382	1	1	2	3	3	4	4	5	6
69	8388	8395	8401	8407	8414	8420	8426	8432	8439	8445	1	1	2	2	3	4	4	5	6
70	8451	8457	8463	8470	8476	8482	8488	8494	8500	8506	1	1	2	2	3	4	4	5	6
71	8513	8519	8525	8531	8537	8543	8549	8555	8561	8567	1	1	2	2	3	4	4	5	5
72	8573	8579	8585	8591	8597	8603	8609	8615	8621	8627	1	1	2	2	3	4	4	5	5
73	8633	8639	8645	8651	8657	8663	8669	8675	8681	8686	1	1	2	2	3	4	4	5	5
74	8692	8698	8704	8710	8716	8722	8727	8733	8739	8745	1	1	2	2	3	4	4	5	5
75	8751	8756	8762	8768	8774	8779	8785	8791	8797	8802	1	1	2	2	3	3	4	5	5
76	8808	8814	8820	8825	8831	8837	8842	8848	8854	8859	1	1	2	2	3	3	4	4	5
77	8865	8871	8876	8882	8887	8893	8899	8904	8910	8915	1	1	2	2	3	3	4	4	5
78	8921	8927	8932	8938	8943	8949	8954	8960	8965	8971	1	1	2	2	3	3	4	4	5
79	8976	8982	8987	8993	8998	9004	9009	9015	9020	9025	1	1	2	2	3	3	4	4	5
80	9031	9036	9042	9047	9053	9058	9063	9069	9074	9079	1	1	2	2	3	3	4	4	5
81	9085	9090	9096	9101	9106	9112	9117	9122	9128	9133	1	1	2	2	3	3	4	4	5
82	9138	9143	9149	9154	9159	9165	9170	9175	9180	9186	1	1	2	2	3	3	4	4	5
83	9191	9196	9201	9206	9212	9217	9222	9227	9232	9238	1	1	2	2	3	3	4	4	5
84	9243	9248	9253	9258	9263	9269	9274	9279	9284	9289	1	1	2	2	3	3	4	4	5
85	9294	9299	9304	9309	9315	9320	9325	9330	9335	9340	1	1	2	2	3	3	4	4	5
86	9345	9350	9355	9360	9365	9370	9375	9380	9385	9390	1	1	2	2	3	3	4	4	5
87	9395	9400	9405	9410	9415	9420	9425	9430	9435	9440	0	1	1	2	2	3	3	4	4
88	9445	9450	9455	9460	9465	9469	9474	9479	9484	9489	0	1	1	2	2	3	3	4	4
89	9494	9499	9504	9509	9513	9518	9523	9528	9533	9538	0	1	1	2	2	3	3	4	4
90	9542	9547	9552	9557	9562	9566	9571	9576	9581	9586	0	1	1	2	2	3	3	4	4
91	9590	9595	9600	9605	9609	9614	9619	9624	9628	9633	0	1	1	2	2	3	3	4	4
92	9638	9643	9647	9652	9657	9661	9666	9671	9675	9680	0	1	1	2	2	3	3	4	4
93	9685	9689	9694	9699	9703	9708	9713	9717	9722	9727	0	1	1	2	2	3	3	4	4
94	9731	9736	9741	9745	9750	9754	9759	9763	9768	9773	0	1	1	2	2	3	3	4	4
95	9777	9782	9786	9791	9795	9800	9805	9809	9814	9818	0	1	1	2	2	3	3	4	4
96	9823	9827	9832	9836	9841	9845	9850	9854	9859	9863	0	1	1	2	2	3	3	4	4
97	9868	9872	9877	9881	9886	9890	9894	9899	9903	9908	0	1	1	2	2	3	3	4	4
98	9912	9917	9921	9926	9930	9934	9939	9943	9948	9952	0	1	1	2	2	3	3	4	4
99	9956	9961	9965	9969	9974	9978	9983	9987	9991	9996	0	1	1	2	2	3	3	3	4
	0	1	2	3	4	5	6												

LABORATORY EXPERIMENTS

IN

ELEMENTARY PHYSICS

THE MACMILLAN COMPANY
NEW YORK · BOSTON · CHICAGO · DALLAS
ATLANTA · SAN FRANCISCO

MACMILLAN AND CO., Limited
LONDON · BOMBAY · CALCUTTA · MADRAS
MELBOURNE

THE MACMILLAN COMPANY
OF CANADA, Limited
TORONTO

MICROMETER AND VERNIER CALIPERS.

Instruments for precise measurement.

LABORATORY EXPERIMENTS IN ELEMENTARY PHYSICS

TO ACCOMPANY

BLACK AND DAVIS' "ELEMENTARY PRACTICAL PHYSICS"

By

NEWTON HENRY BLACK

ASSISTANT PROFESSOR OF PHYSICS
HARVARD UNIVERSITY

THE MACMILLAN COMPANY

New York   1945

PREFACE

THIS book is offered as a guide to both student and instructor in the laboratory work which should accompany BLACK AND DAVIS' *Elementary Practical Physics*. It is the result of many years' experience in teaching physics to beginners. While writing it we have tried to bear in mind present conditions in our schools and colleges — large classes, shortened periods, and the popular demand for "some science for everybody." We know too that many physics teachers carry too heavy a teaching load. We have therefore made every effort to simplify the mechanics of laboratory procedure without sacrificing the valuable educational training that the student gets in doing experiments himself.

In each experiment we have explained just why it is worth doing, what its purpose is, what is to be done, what computations are to be made, and what kinds of results are to be expected. We believe that a tabulated form for data adds to the clearness of a report. But gradually suggestions on form have been abbreviated or omitted in order to give the student some practice in organizing his results for himself. In the same way, we have at first led the student step by step in his computations but have then gradually omitted details. So also in drawing conclusions from experimental data, we have at first asked very definite questions (printed *in italics*) to be answered by the student in complete statements. The stress, we think, should be on logical conclusions based on the experimental facts obtained.

With these ends in view we have again and again revised the directions as experience showed the need of making them so clear that they would not be misunderstood if carefully read and followed. The diagrams have in general been made from photographs of the apparatus as set up for use. We find that such illustrations make it possible to eliminate tedious descriptions. The thirty experiments which we consider *basic* are marked in the table of contents with an asterisk (*), and these will doubtless be included in any well-balanced list of experiments. Of the other experiments we have marked sixteen as *supplementary* because they require more skill in manipulation and rather expensive apparatus. These are intended for the gifted student in a well-equipped laboratory. It is hoped that many of the experiments which are not performed by the students will be done by the instructors as *class demonstrations*. Since the 50-minute laboratory period is all too common in these days of educational pressure and economy, we have divided the directions by four asterisks **** into two parts: the first part is fundamental and to be required of all students; the second part is more or less optional, depending on the time allowance, laboratory equipment, and maturity of the students. In some of the experiments for which there are several forms of excellent apparatus available, we have indicated alternative methods.

It is our experience that students enjoy doing laboratory experiments. They feel that they are really learning physics when making physical measurements themselves. We have tried to show them that physical laws are based on just such experiments, repeated again and again but with more precise apparatus and with greater precautions. Moreover, we are sure that the student in the laboratory can get the experimental point of view and the spirit of inquiry even though we have no psychological test with which to measure this valuable product.

We have been greatly helped in making this book by our colleagues from far and near. Especially would we mention

Professor *Emeritus* Edwin H. Hall of Harvard University for his *Descriptive List of Elementary Exercises in Physics.* We have also received valuable suggestions from Mr. J. Hawley Aiken, Technical High School, Springfield, Mass.; Mr. Edwin Betz, High School, Bethlehem, N. H.; Mr. F. G. Brady, High School, Ashton, Idaho; Mr. Alfred F. Gay, High School, Groveland, Mass.; Mr. Henry M. Hills, Senior High School, San Bernardino, Calif.; Mr. Irwin H. Hoxie, Hardwick Academy, Hardwick, Vt.; Mr. Augustus Klock, Fieldston School, New York City; Mr. Homer W. LeSourd, Milton Academy, Milton, Mass.; Mr. O. A. Martinetti, High School, Chester, Vt.; Mr. Fred Miller, English High School, Boston, Mass.; Mr. M. E. Post, High School, Berkeley, Calif.; Mr. Elbert C. Weaver, Bulkeley High School, Hartford, Conn. We are greatly indebted to Mr. Fred Schueler of the Jefferson Physical Laboratory for his skill in making apparatus and photographs.

TABLE OF CONTENTS

(*First Half Year*)

MECHANICS

BLOCK I. MEASUREMENT. SIMPLE MACHINE ELEMENTS

BLOCK II. MECHANICS OF FLUIDS. PROPERTIES OF MATTER

BLOCK III. FORCES AND MOTIONS

(*Second Half Year*)

MAGNETISM AND ELECTRICITY

SOUND

BLOCK VII. SOUND WAVES AND MUSIC

LIGHT

BLOCK VIII. LIGHT WAVES AND THEIR USES

MODERN PHYSICS

BLOCK IX. RADIO AND RADIUM

NOTE. The thirty experiments marked with an asterisk (*) are considered *basic experiments*. Those experiments marked with the letter (s) are *supplementary* and require more expensive apparatus.

LABORATORY EXPERIMENTS IN ELEMENTARY PHYSICS

INTRODUCTION

SUGGESTIONS TO TEACHERS

It is now more than fifty years since we began to teach elementary physics in the laboratory. Every teacher undoubtedly takes up the task of organizing his laboratory with great enthusiasm and high hopes. Sooner or later, however, he finds that teaching young people physics by means of laboratory exercises involves some difficult problems. For it takes more than costly apparatus and elaborate laboratory directions to produce that mental activity and curiosity about physical phenomena that we all want to stimulate in our students.

Preparing the way. Doubtless the ideal procedure would be that each teacher make his own laboratory manual. Many have done so. This book is the result of one teacher's attempt to select a set of experiments that represent a well-balanced course. The aim has been to make the directions so clear and concise that the average boy or girl who has in mind a general outline of the problem will not only be able to do the experiment but will catch the spirit of scientific investigation. It is assumed that when the class assembles for the laboratory exercise, the teacher will first ask a few questions which will make clear what the problem of the day is and how it is related to the previous work and to the practical affairs of life ; then he will *briefly* outline just how the problem is to be attacked in the laboratory. If the student already has the written directions thoroughly in mind, he

1

ought to be able to proceed with the experiment intelligently and expeditiously.

Recording the results. One reason why so much of our laboratory work in elementary physics is ineffective is that students lose their way in the multitude of details and miss the point or purpose of the experiment. Sometimes they are given directions with such minuteness that their work becomes purely mechanical. This is reflected in their notebooks, which show no individuality and seem to indicate that the work has consisted merely in filling in certain blank spaces in a tabular form. The student will of course at first need much help in arranging his notes in an orderly way; but such suggestions should become unnecessary as time goes on. The great danger in notebook work is artificiality. The student should write out his notes in his own words and in such form that when he reviews his work six months or a year later they will recall to his mind just what he did and what his results were.

Degree of accuracy. In the early days of student laboratory work, a very large part of the time devoted to physics was spent in the laboratory. But in recent years we have come to believe that many subjects can best be presented in their *qualitative* aspects in clean-cut classroom demonstrations by the teacher and that the work of the student in the laboratory should be to perform a few well-selected experiments involving simple measurements. In this connection it must always be remembered that the student is primarily learning not to make physical *measurements* but to use *physics*. Therefore it is hardly worth while at this stage to spend much time in discussing percentage errors which are to be reckoned, for instance, in tenths of one per cent. The engineer often has to be satisfied with results which check within five per cent. Why should we seek for such a high degree of accuracy as can be attained only by complicating the apparatus and the manipulation?

Correlation of laboratory work. Inspectors of the science work done in our secondary schools report that much of it fails because the laboratory work is not closely related to the recitations and class discussions and, what is still more important, to the needs and interests of the student. The laboratory problems should provide direct and obvious connections between what immediately precedes and follows. The student should go to the laboratory to find out by experiment some facts that are essential to the solution of a real physics problem. As far as possible these experiments should deal with the mechanisms and appliances of everyday experience. When all is said and done, however, it must be borne in mind that the successful correlation of laboratory work with the rest of a student's instruction and life depends not on books or apparatus but on the *teacher*.

SUGGESTIONS TO STUDENTS

Follow directions. Before beginning an experiment, carefully read the directions through in order to have a clear idea of (1) *what you are to do* and (2) *how you are to do it*. Then read the directions again and follow each word closely. For these directions have been carefully framed to prevent your wasting time and making needless mistakes. *Every word is significant.*

Check up your apparatus. You will notice that at the beginning of each experiment there is a list of the apparatus needed in that particular experiment. It will save time if you first run through the list and make sure that you have at hand on your table each article there specified and that it is in good condition.

Errors in observation. All physical measurements are subject to accidental errors in observation due to unknown causes; therefore absolute accuracy can in no case be expected. The effect of such errors on the result can, however, be largely eliminated by taking the mean of several observations. But every observation that is made should be wholly uninfluenced by any previous observation or by a tendency, often unconscious, to make all results agree. All observers have a tendency to record, not what they see, but what they think they should see. Learn to be strictly honest with yourself!

Relative importance of accuracy. Although it is very desirable that the final result of an experiment should be as accurate as possible, yet this does not mean that every observation must be taken with the greatest care. Those observations which are liable to contain *the greatest percentage of error* will produce the greatest error in the final result and must therefore be taken with the greatest care. The final result cannot be more accurate than the least accurate factor.

Laboratory notebook. Whatever the form of notebook used, it should contain a careful record of (*a*) what you actually do, (*b*) what you actually observe, and (*c*) what conclusions you can draw from your own experimental facts.

(1) It is well to arrange your notebook in an orderly fashion. Begin each experiment on a new page and record first the date on which each experiment is performed as well as the number, title, and purpose of the experiment.

(2) Then put down all the measurements and facts which you have observed, recording each measurement as soon as you have made it, and *recording it just as you have made it* whether it seems to you at the time reasonable or not. The numbers thus recorded should not be the result of additions or subtractions done in your head. The original observations should never be trusted to loose sheets of paper, backs of envelopes, etc.

(3) Next compute the result which may reasonably be derived from the data at hand. In this arithmetical work arrange your computations in an orderly fashion so that it will be evident to anyone who examines the book just

what your process has been. Be particularly careful not to crowd this work, to make very clear and legible figures, and to attach to each result its proper unit. Remember that decimal fractions are much more convenient to handle than common fractions, and that the use of *logarithms* or a *slide rule* will shorten the labor involved.

(4) It will be found that a carefully made diagram of the apparatus with descriptive labels attached will often be sufficient to show the method of carrying on the experiment. If this is not enough, add a few clear statements to show the method used.

(5) State the general conclusions which may be drawn from your experiment, and be careful to draw no conclusions which your facts do not warrant. In answering the questions suggested by the experiment, make complete sentences of such a sort that there is no trouble later in recalling the nature of each question.

Significant figures. A physical quantity should be recorded just as accurately as it has been measured. For example, 7.40 cm. in the record of an experiment does not mean exactly the same thing as 7.4 cm. The *first* record shows that the hundredths of a centimeter could be estimated, and that the length was estimated to be more nearly 7.40 cm. than 7.41 cm. or 7.39 cm. The *second* record means that the hundredths of a centimeter were not taken into account.

Suppose we find that three measurements of the same dimension give 12.55 cm., 12.58 cm., and 12.57 cm. In this case we are sure of the first three figures, 12.5, but the fourth figure was estimated and therefore is **doubtful**. To find the mean value we find the sum of these numbers, which is 37.70 cm., and then divide by 3. The mean value might be written 12.5666+ cm., but *this is not justifiable* because it assumes greater accuracy than the measurements warrant. We should keep *but one doubtful figure* in the mean value.

that is, the first 6, and drop the rest; but since the next figure is 5 or more, we call the doubtful figure one more. The mean value should be given as **12.57 cm.**

Remember that the position of the decimal point has nothing whatever to do with the significance of figures. For example, the wave length of sodium light is 0.00005893 centimeters. The first five ciphers serve to locate the decimal point. The figures 589 are sure, and the 3 is doubtful.

Percentage of error. The actual error to be expected in a physical measurement may be large, as, for example, 4 or 5 feet in measuring the velocity of sound; or it may be small, as, for example, 1 or 2 thousandths of an inch in measuring the diameter of a wire. The difference between your experimental result and the accepted value (which has generally been obtained by a trained observer making a large number of trials with high-grade instruments) is called the *actual error*. But it is a much more significant expression of the degree of accuracy to find what fraction (expressed as percentage) this actual error is of the accepted value. For example, suppose the velocity of sound under certain conditions is 1127 feet per second and your experimental result is 1132 feet per second. Then your actual error is 5 feet per second, which seems at first sight a big error. But the *percentage of error* is $\frac{5}{1127} \times 100$, or about 0.4%. *To find the percentage of error, divide the actual error by the accepted value, and multiply the quotient by 100.*

It is impossible to state a uniform rule for the degree of accuracy to be expected in all the experiments in this book. The type of apparatus used and the conditions under which the experiment is performed must be considered. It is to be hoped that the results will not show an error of more than 1 per cent, but in certain experiments, such as those on friction, the errors may run to 5 per cent. Aim for the best results and try to improve in accuracy, but whatever you do, be honest with yourself in all your results.

Care of apparatus. Remember that the success of any experiment depends upon *two factors:* the form and accuracy of the *apparatus* and the skill of the *manipulator* in handling the apparatus. Every graduated instrument is more or less in error, but if you know the precision which you may reasonably expect to get from it and then work for that precision, you will be doing all that can be expected. Experience shows that students often blame the apparatus for their poor results when really the fault is due to their own arithmetical mistakes in computation or their carelessness in the use of the apparatus. *Make each piece do its work to the limit.*

When your experiment is completed, be sure to leave your apparatus in good condition. Report to the instructor in charge anything which seems to be out of adjustment.

MECHANICS

BLOCK I. MEASUREMENT. SIMPLE MACHINE ELEMENTS

Suggestive Questions*

1. *Why do we have standards of length, weight, and time?*
2. *Why is the metric system of units an international system?*
3. *Why is every measurement more or less inaccurate?*
4. *What is meant by the tolerance allowed in machine construction?*
5. *How can one measure the diameter of a steel rod to one-tenth of a millimeter?*
6. *How can a claw hammer exert a pull of half a ton?*
7. *How would you move a barn with block and tackle?*
8. *Why is it advantageous to place the load on a wheelbarrow near the wheel?*
9. *What is lost in a machine because of friction?*
10. *In what two ways is friction utilized in an automobile?*
11. *Why do you shift gears in driving an automobile up a steep grade?*
12. *In what ways is the modern automobile engine said to be equivalent to 100 horses?*
13. *In what ways is a can opener like a steam shovel?*
14. *Why is the rear sprocket of a bicycle about one-third the size of the front one?*
15. *Which is more important, a large mechanical advantage or a high mechanical efficiency?*

* NOTE TO TEACHERS. These are provocative questions which, it is hoped, will stir up class discussions. They will reveal how much general information about the simple machine elements may be assumed.

EXPERIMENT 1

MEASUREMENT OF LENGTH IN THE METRIC SYSTEM

How accurately can you measure the sides of a right triangle?
How accurately can you measure the circumference and diameter
of a circle?

Triangle, celluloid   30-centimeter rule   Protractor

Introduction. The metric system is the one that is generally used in the laboratory and with a little practice we shall learn to apply it with even more precision than our familiar English system. Its great advantage lies in the fact that, like our numbers, it is a decimal system and so is extremely easy to use. This experiment will serve as a brief review of the metric system and will give us an opportunity to learn to measure distances more accurately than heretofore. However, we must not be discouraged to find that all of our measurements are more or less inaccurate. It will accordingly be one of our tasks to determine how precise each measurement is.

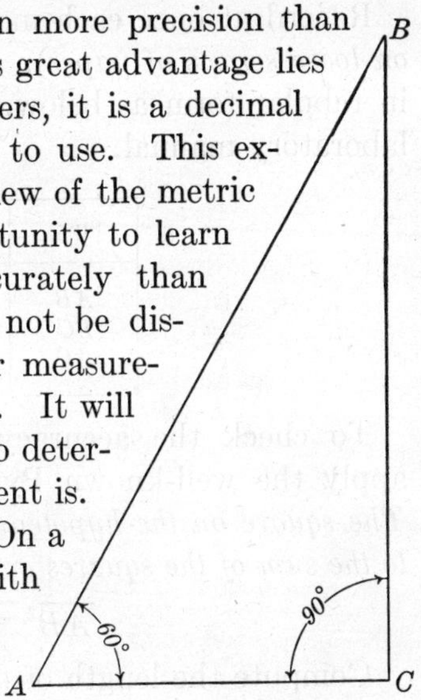

Directions. *Right triangle.* On a page in your notebook draw with a sharp, hard lead pencil a straight line *AC*, 8 to 10 centimeters in length. At *A* construct with your protractor an

Fig. 1–1.   A right triangle.

angle of 60° and at *C* an angle of 90°. Extend these lines until they intersect at *B*, making a right triangle *ABC* (Fig. 1–1).

9

Measure each of the three sides with great care and record each length in centimeters and a decimal fraction of a centimeter. Note first the whole number of centimeters, then the number of millimeters, which are expressed as tenths of a centimeter (0.1 cm.), and lastly the tenths of a millimeter, which are to be estimated * and expressed as hundredths of a centimeter (0.01 cm.). *Always express a fraction as a decimal.* If it should happen that the end of a line exactly coincides with a millimeter mark on the rule, then record a zero in the hundredths place, thus, 12.30 cm.; and if it should happen that the end coincides with a centimeter mark on the rule, then record zeros in *both* the tenths and hundredths places, thus, 12.00 cm. This shows that we have measured the length to a hundredth of a centimeter.

Record at once each measurement in your notebook (*not on loose scraps of paper*). It is well to arrange your record in tabular form as below. Write nothing whatever in the laboratory manual.

SIDES	LENGTHS
AB	— —.— — cm.
BC	— —.— — cm.
AC	— —.— — cm.

To check the accuracy of these measurements, let us apply the well-known Pythagorean theorem in geometry: *The square on the hypotenuse of a right triangle is equivalent to the sum of the squares on the two sides.* That is,

$$\overline{AB}^2 = \overline{AC}^2 + \overline{BC}^2$$

Compute the length of the side AB from the above equation and compare the result with the length of the side AB as obtained by direct measurement. *How do you account for the discrepancy?*

* It will be useful to remember that one-half a millimeter is equal to 0.05 cm. and that 0.02 cm. is a little less than a quarter of a millimeter.

Perform all your computations in your notebook and arrange your work in an orderly fashion. It is suggested that you show the results of your computations as follows:

$$\overline{AC}^2 = ——.——\ \text{cm.}^2$$
$$\overline{BC}^2 = ——.——\ \text{cm.}^2$$
$$\overline{AC}^2 + \overline{BC}^2 = ——.——\ \text{cm.}^2$$
$$AB = \sqrt{\overline{AC}^2 + \overline{BC}^2} = ——.——\ \text{cm. (By computation.)}$$
$$AB = ——.——\ \text{cm. (By measurement.)}$$
$$\text{Difference} = ——.——\ \text{cm.}$$

Another check can easily be applied to this triangle. It is a geometrical fact that *in a right triangle with angles 30° and 60°, the hypotenuse is just twice the length of the shortest side.* That is,

$$AB = 2\ AC$$

Compare the length of AB and $2 \times AC$ and record the difference. If there is a difference of more than 2 millimeters, check again with your protractor the angles A and C.

*   *   *   *

Circle.* Measure the diameter of a circular disk or of a large brass weight with great care. Estimate to one one-hundredth of a centimeter (0.01 cm.). To measure the circumference of the cylinder, wrap tightly around it a strip of thin paper and with a pin prick a hole through the paper where it overlaps, as shown in figure 1–2. Measure carefully the distance between these two pinholes. Record your measurements thus:

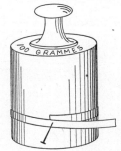

Fig. 1–2. Measuring the circumference of a cylinder.

Diameter $= ——.——$ cm.
Circumference $= ——.——$ cm.

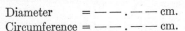

* If the time allowed for your laboratory work permits, it is well to do this second part of the experiment.

To check the accuracy of these measurements, let us apply another geometrical principle : *The number obtained by dividing the circumference of any circle by its diameter is approximately* 3.14. This number is denoted by the Greek letter π (pronounced pī).

Compute the value of π from your values of the circumference and the diameter. Record the results thus :

$$\pi = \frac{\text{circumference}}{\text{diameter}} = \text{—} \cdot \text{— —} \quad \text{(By experiment.)}$$

$$\text{True value of } \pi = 3.14. \qquad \text{(By geometry.)}$$

$$\text{Difference, or error, } = \text{—} \cdot \text{— —}$$

Discussion :

(a) *Why do we use decimals instead of common fractions in the metric system?*

(b) *Does the truth of the Pythagorean theorem depend upon measurements?*

(c) *In determining the value of π, which measurement should be made with the greater care? Why?*

(d) *What are some of the possible sources of error in your determination of the value of π?*

EXPERIMENT 2

DENSITY OF WOODS AND METALS

What is the average weight in grams of one cubic centimeter of wood?

Rectangular block of wood, such as maple, oak, pine
Blocks or cylinders of metals, such as iron, brass, aluminum

30-cm. rule
Platform or spring balance
Set of weights

Introduction. Density means the weight per unit volume of a substance. Therefore we must get the weight and the volume of the sample block, and then we can easily compute the weight of one cubic centimeter. Density is one of the important characteristics of materials.

Our first problem is to find the density of a certain block of wood. Different kinds of wood have different densities. For example, poplar has a density of 0.35 gram per cubic centimeter, whereas black ironwood has a density of 1.27 grams per cubic centimeter.

The block of wood, although apparently rectangular, is not geometrically perfect, and therefore it will be necessary to make several measurements of its length, width, and thickness. Then we can compute the average, or mean, length, width, and thickness, and from these values determine the volume of the block. The weight can easily be found by using a platform or spring balance. Finally, we can compute the average weight in grams of one cubic centimeter of the wood.

Directions. First adjust the balance (Fig. 2–1) so that it will just balance evenly with no load in either scalepan. A balance which quickly comes to rest is probably not

13

in first-class condition. Therefore we can judge better whether a balance is swinging evenly by noting the swings of the pans up and down than by noting where it happens to come to rest.

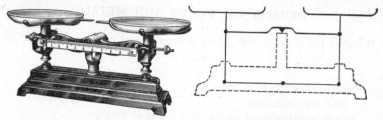

Fig. 2–1. Platform balance with diagram.

Place a block of wood in the left pan (at the zero end of the beam) and counterbalance with weights. Steady the scale-pan with the left hand while adding or removing the larger weights in order to avoid jarring the balance and dulling the knife-edges. It will save time if you begin by using a weight which is probably a bit too heavy and, if so, removing it and replacing it with the next smaller weight. Continue in this way until you have the largest weight which is lighter than the object. Then add the next smaller weight to the scale-pan, and so on until within 10 grams of the weight. Make the final adjustment by using the rider on the beam. Take great care in counting up the weights used. Record this total weight (in grams and decimal fraction) at once in your notebook as the weight of the block.

To measure the block to a hundredth of a centimeter with an ordinary metric rule requires considerable care. The block should be placed on a sheet of white paper in a good light. The measuring stick should be placed along one edge AB of the block so that one end is exactly in line with some centimeter mark, such as the 10-centimeter mark, as shown in figure 2–2. The other end of the block will probably not lie exactly in line with any millimeter mark on the scale, and so it is necessary to estimate the fraction of a millimeter. Express the result as centimeters and a decimal fraction thereof. For example, 12.35 cm.

To get the length, measure each of the four edges parallel to the grain of the wood. It is not likely that all these measurements, if carefully made to a hundredth of a centimeter, will

Fig. 2–2.   Measuring one edge of a block.

give exactly the same result. But we can determine the average length by finding the sum of these four measurements of length and dividing by four.

For example :

$$
\begin{array}{c}
\text{LENGTH} \\
12.35 \text{ cm.} \\
12.37 \text{ cm.} \\
12.33 \text{ cm.} \\
\underline{12.38 \text{ cm.}} \\
4)\overline{49.43 \text{ cm.}} \\
12.357 \text{ cm.}
\end{array}
$$

Average length 12.36 cm.

To get the average width, measure each of the four long edges crosswise to the grain; in a similar manner measure the length of each of the four short edges and thus get the average thickness of the block.

It is very desirable to record all of these measurements in an orderly way, so the following model is suggested :

Weight of block No. —— = ———— . —— g.

LENGTH	WIDTH	THICKNESS
——.—— cm.	——.—— cm.	——.—— cm.
——.—— cm.	——.—— cm.	——.—— cm.
——.—— cm.	——.—— cm.	——.—— cm.
——.—— cm.	——.—— cm.	——.—— cm.
4)————.——	4)————.——	4)————.——
Average ——.—— cm.	Average ——.—— cm.	Average ——.—— cm.

Computation. The volume of a rectangular block is equal to the product of the length × the width × the thickness. In computing the volume of the block it will save time if we retain only **significant figures**; that is, if we retain in the average values for the length, width, and thickness only the first *doubtful figure*. Since the second-place decimal in these measurements was obtained by estimating to one tenth of a millimeter, this figure in each measurement is doubtful. Therefore, even in the average value, there will be some uncertainty about the second decimal place. If the third-place decimal is 5 or more, it is customary to discard it and to add one to the preceding digit, as shown in the illustrative example.

As a general rule, in multiplying numbers together, retain in the product only as many significant figures as there are in the least accurate factor.

In this case the least accurate factor is the shortest side, which is the thickness, and so the final product should have no more figures than this measurement.

Record the results of your computation as follows:

Volume of block = — — — cm.³

$$\text{Density of} \underline{} \text{wood} = \frac{\underline{}.\underline{}\text{ g.}}{\underline{}\text{ cm.}^3} = \underline{}\text{ g./cm.}^3$$

Note about significant figures. Since in each of the above measurements the tenths of a millimeter, that is, the hundredths of a centimeter, had to be estimated, it follows that each measurement is uncertain to at least 0.01 of a centimeter. For example, suppose one edge of the block measured 12.46 centimeters. This would mean that we were certain of the first three digits (12.4) but that the 6 was doubtful and probably somewhat in error. Again, suppose the width of the block measured 10.25 centimeters. This would mean that we were sure of 10.2 but were somewhat uncertain in regard to the final 5.

In each case we are dealing with numbers containing four significant figures, the last digit in each number being somewhat in doubt.

Now it is obvious that when we multiply these two dimensions together, the product will also be somewhat in error. Let us see how much.

12.46	127.7	654)465.7(0.712
10.25	5.12	4578
6230	2554	790
2492	1277	654
1246	6385	1360
127.7150	653.824	1308
		52

In the above computation the doubtful figures are printed in black type. It will be seen that in the product we retain only four figures (127.7), saving only one doubtful figure.

If we suppose the thickness of the block to be 5.12 centimeters, then the volume, as shown above, would be 654 cubic centimeters. In this result we retain only *three* figures because the least accurate factor is the smallest dimension (the thickness), which has but three significant figures. We record 654 instead of 653 because the second doubtful figure eight (0.8) was greater than one half (0.5), and therefore in discarding it we add one unit to the doubtful figure 3, making it 654 cm.[3]

In the same way, when we divide two numbers which are obtained from measurements and so are more or less inaccurate, we keep in the quotient only one doubtful figure. Thus, suppose the weight of the block to be 465.7 grams. To find the density we divide this weight by the volume just computed, and the quotient is 0.712 gram per cubic centimeter. In this quotient we retain but three significant figures because the volume has but three significant figures, and the quotient can be no more accurate than the divisor, as shown above.

In general, then, all numbers obtained from measurements are more or less inaccurate. We may therefore retain as significant figures only one doubtful digit. The result of any arithmetical computation can never be more accurate than its least accurate factor.

* * * *

A more precise experiment. Determine the density of a metal cylinder by measuring its length and diameter with a **vernier caliper.** The volume of a cylinder is equal to the area of base × height. That is,

$$V = \frac{\pi D^2}{4} \times H$$

where V is the volume, D the diameter, and H the height. Then weigh the cylinder as just described and compute the density (grams per cubic centimeter).

Vernier caliper. When a meter stick is used, it is necessary to *estimate* the tenths of a millimeter, the smallest scale

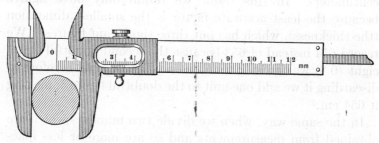

Fig. 2–3. Vernier caliper measures the diameter to 0.01 cm.

division. The vernier is a device which assists in the accurate reading of the fractional part of a scale division. The vernier caliper (Fig. 2–3) has two scales: one is fixed and the other is arranged to slide along the fixed scale. In the metric instrument the fixed scale is divided into centimeters and millimeters, and the sliding scale has 10 divisions which are equal to 9 millimeters. Therefore each division on the sliding scale is equal to 0.9 millimeter. When the jaws are in contact, the zero, or index, mark of the sliding scale coincides with the zero mark on the fixed scale; the first mark of the sliding scale falls short of a mark on the fixed scale by just 0.1 millimeter, and the second mark by 0.2 millimeter, etc. If the movable jaw is moved, say 0.4 millimeter from its zero position, the fourth vernier mark on the sliding scale coincides with a mark on the fixed scale.

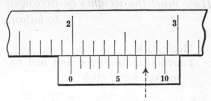

Fig. 2–4. Vernier reads 1.98.

To read the metric vernier caliper, *note the left-hand division on the fixed scale nearest the vernier zero mark* (for example, 1.9 cm. in figure 2–4) *and the vernier division* (8 in this case) *which lies in the same straight line with some fixed-scale division*. (The reading in this case is 1.98 cm.) That division on the sliding scale which coincides with a division on the fixed scale gives the tenths of millimeters or *hundredths of centimeters*.

Many vernier calipers are made with two sets of jaws, one (below) for outside measurements and the other (above) for inside measurements, and a depth gauge (at the right). They are often provided with a double scale, one metric and the other English, reading to $\frac{1}{128}$ of an inch.

THE STRAIGHT LEVER. PRINCIPLE OF MOMENTS

How must the weights be arranged on a straight lever in order to balance?

Meter stick	Set of weights
Fulcrum or clamp rod and nail to support meter stick	Thread, black linen, No. 30

Introduction. A crowbar is perhaps the most familiar example of a straight lever. The problem often arises how to use such a bar so that by applying a given effort (one's own weight) at one end a given load may be lifted at the other end. To solve such problems we must understand the **principle of moments**. The moment of a weight is its turning effect, which depends on its **weight** and its **distance** from the fulcrum. Thus,

$$\text{Moment} = \text{weight} \times \text{distance.}$$

In this experiment we shall compare the moments of the weights tending to turn the lever in one direction with the moments of the weights tending to turn the lever in the opposite direction.

Directions. Suspend or support a meter stick at its midpoint. If it does not quite balance, place a rider made of a bent piece of sheet metal on the lighter side at such a point as to produce equilibrium. Hang at A by a thread a 100-gram weight W_1 at a distance of 40 centimeters d_1 to the left of the fulcrum F, and then hang at B a 200-gram weight W_2 at some point on the other side so as to balance it (Fig. 3–1). It is not necessary to wait for the lever to come to rest; for it is in equilibrium when it swings through equal distances on opposite sides of the horizontal position. Record these weights W_1 and W_2 and their corresponding distances from the fulcrum as d_1 and d_2.

Repeat, using a different set of weights, and record both the weights and their distances from the fulcrum.

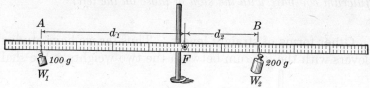

Fig. 3-1. Straight lever with unequal weights. $W_1 \times d_1 = W_2 \times d_2$.

Then hang two weights W_2 and W_3 at different points on the same side of the fulcrum and balance them with a single weight W_1 on the other side. Record the weights and their distances from the fulcrum.

Arrange these data in some convenient tabular form such as the following:

TRIALS	W_1	d_1	W_2	d_2	W_3	d_3
1					—	—
2					—	—
3						

Computation. Calculate the moment of each of these weights about the fulcrum as follows:

	$W_1 \times d_1$	$W_2 \times d_2$	$W_3 \times d_3$
Trial 1	— × — = —	— × — = —	
Trial 2	— × — = —	— × — = —	
Trial 3	— × — = —	— × — = —	— × — = —

Results. Answer the following questions in complete sentences.

(a) *What relation seems to exist between the moment of the weight on the right and that of the weight on the left of the fulcrum? Compare $W_1 \times d_1$ and $W_2 \times d_2$.*

(*b*) *Are the differences between the moments on both sides of the fulcrum greater than would be expected from the experimental errors?*

(*c*) *How does the sum of the moments on the right of the fulcrum compare with the sum of those on the left?*

*   *   *   *

Other forms of straight levers. Thus far we have studied levers with the fulcrum between the two weights. We shall

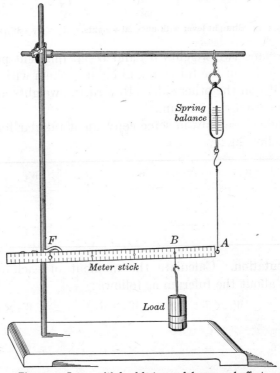

Fig. 3–2.   Lever with load between fulcrum and effort.

now consider a case where the fulcrum is at one end and the effort or upward pull is exerted at the other end. The weight or load is placed somewhere in between. We shall use only the right half of our meter stick in figure 3–2. The fulcrum F is at the left and the effort A is at the right end. First we note the reading of the spring balance when we place the load W at B. Then we compute the moment of this force about the fulcrum F and the moment of the weight W about the same point. *Compare these two moments.*

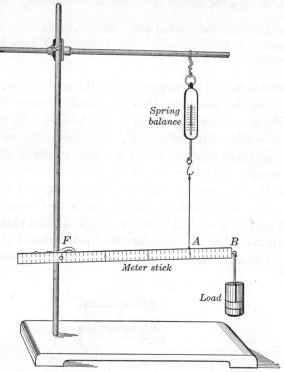

Fig. 3–3. Lever with effort between load and fulcrum.

Repeat this experiment with the load W at the end of the stick and with the effort A between the fulcrum and the load (Fig. 3–3). *Compare the moment of the effort and the moment of the weight.*

EXPERIMENT 4

WEIGHT OF A LEVER AND ITS CENTER OF GRAVITY

Where may the weight of a lever be considered to act?

Meter stick loaded at one end with   Set of weights
   a block of lead   Thread, black linen, No. 30
Triangular block of wood

Introduction. In Experiment 3 we did not have to consider the effect of the weight of the lever itself because the lever was uniform and was balanced in the middle. In practical work the weight of the lever itself often has to be considered, and our problem now is to find out how to make allowance for the weight of the lever. It would be very convenient if we could find one point at which we could consider the whole weight to be concentrated, that is, as if the lever weighed nothing and as if we had another weight at this point.

Directions. Let us consider the loaded meter stick AL (Fig. 4–1) as an example of a nonuniform lever whose weight

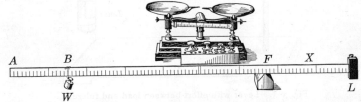

Fig. 4–1. Weight of lever acts at X.

cannot be neglected. Hang a known weight W at some fixed point B. Now slide the meter stick along the triangular block of wood F until the whole thing just balances. Then the moment of W about F is equal to $W \times BF$.

Let us call the center of weight of the lever itself, if there is one, X and its distance from the fulcrum FX. Then its

24

moment is equal to the *weight of the lever* $\times FX$.   But this moment is equal to the moment on the other side $W \times BF$. In other words, we have

$$\textit{Wt. of lever} \times FX = W \times BF.$$

If we know the weight of the lever, we can compute the value FX and determine the position of X on the meter stick.

First weigh the loaded meter stick to the nearest tenth of a gram.   Then attach by a thread a 100-gram weight W to the meter stick at B, 10 centimeters from the end A.   Balance the whole thing on the block F as a fulcrum.   Note the distance AF of the fulcrum from the end of the meter stick.

Repeat this experiment several times with different known weights at various positions, but each time determining the distance AF.

Computation.   First find the distance of the known weight W from the fulcrum F, or BF.   From this calculate the moment of W about F, that is, find the product $W \times BF$. Then, knowing the weight of the lever, we may calculate its acting distance FX from the fulcrum.   That is,

$$FX = \frac{W \times BF}{Wt.\ of\ lever}.$$

From this we can find the position of X on the meter stick, or the distance AX.

Compare the various positions of X, the center of weight of the lever itself, as determined in the several trials.

Finally, balance on the block F the lever alone without W. This position of F, where the lever balances on a knife-edge, is called its *center of gravity*.   Note the distance of this center of gravity from the end A of the meter stick.

It will be well to arrange the data and computations in tabular form somewhat as follows:

Weight of the loaded lever ———g

DATA			COMPUTATIONS			
W	AB	AF	BF	$BF \times W$	$FX = \dfrac{BF \times W}{Wt.\ of\ lever}$	AX
100 g.	10.0 cm.					
200 g.	10.0 cm.					
200 g.	15.0 cm.					
500 g.						

Center of gravity (CG) is located —— cm. from A.

Results. (a) *Does the weight of the lever act as if concentrated at one point?*

(b) *Does the weight of the lever act as if concentrated at the center of gravity?*

* * * *

Applications of levers. Applying the results of this experiment, find the weight of the lever by balancing it against a known weight. Compare this computed weight with the actual weight as determined by the platform scales.

Also apply the results of this experiment to find the weight of an iron ball by balancing it against the known weight of a lever. Compare this computed weight with the actual weight as determined by the platform scales. Draw carefully labeled diagrams showing dimensions.

EXPERIMENT 5

PARALLEL FORCES AND MOMENTS

What two conditions must always exist in order to have parallel forces in equilibrium?

2 Spring balances (2000 g.)   Meter stick
Set of weights   Thread, black linen, No. 30

Introduction. When a truck moves across a bridge, how is its weight distributed on the two supports at the ends of the bridge? When two men carry a heavy weight on a stick between them, how does the upward pull exerted by each man depend on the position of the weight?

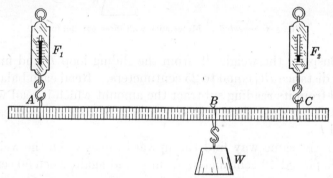

Fig. 5-1. Meter stick with three parallel forces.

We may study such problems by suspending a meter stick from two spring balances in a horizontal position and then attaching one or more weights at various points along the stick (Fig. 5-1). In each case we shall (1) compare the sum of the forces acting in one direction with the sum of the forces acting in the opposite direction, and (2) compare the sum of the moments of the forces tending to produce clockwise rotation with the sum of the moments of the forces tending to produce counterclockwise rotation about a point.

Directions. Hang two spring balances F_1 and F_2 from some convenient support * and suspend a meter stick from the hooks of the balances, as shown in figure 5–1. Read and record the forces required to support the stick alone.

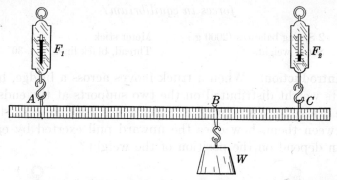

Fig. 5–1 (*repeated*). Meter stick with three parallel forces.

Suspend the weight W from the sliding loop B and make the distance BC equal to 25 centimeters. Read each balance and from its reading subtract the amount which it read with the meter stick alone. Record these results as the forces F_1 and F_2.

In the same way find the upward forces when the weight W is placed 40 centimeters from C and again when 50 centimeters.

Finally, hang two weights from the stick and determine the upward forces needed to support them.

Make a simple diagram in each case, indicating the distances on the meter stick by dimension lines and representing the forces by arrows drawn to a scale which will be specified by your instructor. Also note the amount of each force at the right of the arrow representing it.

* In case there is no convenient support for the balances, the experiment may be done by using 4 spring balances and arranging the apparatus flat on the table with clamps to hold the balances.

Computation. Compute in each case the sum of the upward forces and compare with the downward force or forces (weights).

Compute the moment of each force about A. Find in each case the sum of the moments tending to produce clockwise rotation and the sum of the moments tending to produce counterclockwise rotation about the same point A.

Repeat the computations in one case, using some other point, such as C, as the axis of rotation.

Results. When several parallel forces are in equilibrium, (a) *how does the sum of the forces acting in one direction compare with the sum of the forces acting in the opposite direction?*

(b) *How does the sum of the moments of the forces tending to produce clockwise rotation about any given point compare with the sum of the moments of the forces tending to produce counterclockwise rotation about the same point?*

State your answers in complete sentences.

*   *   *   *

Balanced couples. When two equal parallel forces acting in opposite directions are applied to a body at points some distance apart, they tend to make the body rotate. Such a pair of forces constitutes a **couple.** No single force can balance a couple, but a second couple can do so if it tends to make the body rotate in the opposite direction.

We may study the conditions of equilibrium of couples by placing a square board on steel balls and then by applying forces A, B, C,

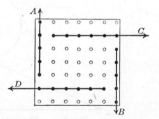

Fig. 5–2. Four forces at right angles.

and D to inserted pegs, as shown in figure 5–2. Vary the tension on the balances until the forces act along the cross lines of the board. Notice that force $A = B$ and force $C = D$. Record the forces, their points of application, and their directions on a diagram.   Take some peg as the turning point. Compute the sum of the moments clockwise and also the sum of the moments counterclockwise about this point. Compare these sums.   Repeat the computation using some other peg as the turning point.

Try another case with the pegs in different positions.

EXPERIMENT 6

WORK DONE ON AN INCLINED PLANE

How much work is required to pull a loaded car up an inclined plane?

Smooth board about 100 cm. long	Fixed pulley at end of board
Support for one end	or spring balance (2000 g.)
Car (Hall's) with cord attached	Set of weights or other load

Meter stick

Introduction.   Everyone is familiar with the fact that it is easier to roll a barrel of flour up an inclined plank from the sidewalk into a truck than it is to lift the barrel straight up. But how about the amount of work done?   Technically work

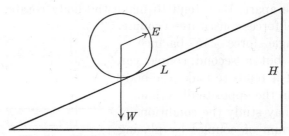

Fig. 6–1.   Work done in rolling a barrel up an incline.

means the overcoming of resistance.   A barrel of flour resists being lifted because it is attracted by the earth.   We can measure the work done in lifting the barrel straight up by multiplying the weight W by the height H (Fig. 6–1).   For example, 200 pounds lifted 3 feet would require 3×200, or 600 foot-pounds of work. But when the barrel is rolled up a plank, the force required is less and the distance is greater. The work done is the product of this force E times the length of the inclined plane L. We wish to compare the amounts of work in both cases, that is, the two products $W \times H$ and $E \times L$.

Directions. In this experiment we shall pull a loaded car up a board placed in a slanting position. We may use a fixed pulley * at the upper end of the board and hang on

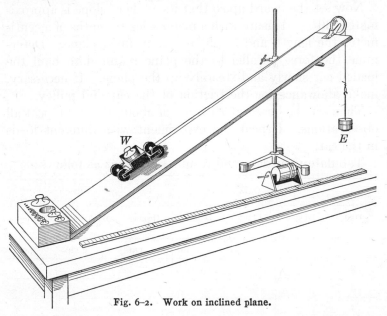

Fig. 6-2. Work on inclined plane.

enough weights E to draw the car up the incline (Fig. 6-2). The weight of the car and its load is the weight W which is lifted. To measure the slope of the board, measure the length L along the board and measure the height H of the lower surface of the board at the upper end above the table.

* Sometimes it is more convenient to perform this experiment by using a spring balance instead of a fixed pulley and weights at the upper end of the incline.

Certain precautions should be observed.   First, determine whether friction plays a large part in the effort required to pull the car up the incline.   Evidently this effort will be a little more than if friction could be entirely eliminated. But if the car is allowed slowly to roll down the incline, the effort required to hold it back will be slightly less because of the friction.   One half the difference between these two pulls is the force required to overcome friction.   If this friction is very small, it may be disregarded.

Now set the board up so that its angle of slope is approximately 30°.   Measure with a meter stick to tenths of a centimeter the length and height of the inclined plane.   Determine the force parallel to the plane required to haul the loaded car slowly and steadily up the plane.   If necessary, make allowance for the friction of the car and pulley.

Then set the board at an angle of about 45° and repeat all observations.   Repeat the experiment with different loads in the car.

Tabulate your data and results somewhat as follows :

DATA					RESULTS	
Trial	Weight W	Effort E	Length L	Height H	Work done $W \times H$	Work put in $E \times L$
1	g.	g.	cm.	cm.	g.cm.	g.cm.
2						
3						
4						

Results.   Compare in each trial the *work accomplished* in lifting the car and its load straight up $(W \times H)$ with the *work expended* in pulling the car up the incline $(E \times L)$, assuming that friction has been eliminated.

Compare in each trial the *mechanical advantage*, that is, the ratio of weight lifted to effort applied $\left(\dfrac{W}{E}\right)$ with the *velocity ratio*, that is, the ratio of the distance which the effort moves to the corresponding distance which the weight is lifted $\left(\dfrac{L}{H}\right)$.

EXPERIMENT 7

SLIDING FRICTION

How does starting friction compare with sliding friction?
How great is the coefficient of sliding friction for leather on wood?

Board with a smooth surface	Set of weights
Wooden box with pieces of leather glued	Spring balance (2000 g.)
to the bottom (Gilley)	Meter stick

Introduction. The fan on an automobile is driven from the crankshaft by means of a belt. The effectiveness of this method of transmitting power to the fan depends on the friction between the belt and pulleys. In the same way the usefulness of the brakes on an automobile depends on friction between the brake lining and the steel drum. In fact, the automobile could not propel itself along the road except for the friction between the tires on the driving (rear) wheels and the road.

On the other hand, it is one of the great problems of the mechanical engineer to eliminate or reduce to a minimum friction in machines. This is because friction reduces the efficiency of a machine since some work must be done against friction, which is usually wasted as heat. Besides, the friction causes much wear on the rubbing surfaces.

By friction we mean the resistance encountered when we attempt to slide one surface over another. The force necessary to overcome friction depends upon so many conditions, such as the materials, the nature of the surfaces, the lubrication, and the force pushing the surfaces together, that it is very difficult to make any general or exact statements about friction. However, in this experiment we shall be able to compare the force needed to start a body sliding on a horizontal surface with that required to keep it sliding. We shall also determine the ratio between the force required to keep a body sliding and the perpendicular force holding the surfaces in contact, that is, the *coefficient of sliding friction.*

Directions. *On a horizontal plane.* Find the weight of the wooden box by means of a spring balance. Place the board on the table and set the friction box upon it. By

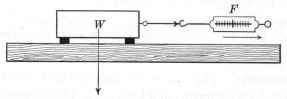

Fig 7–1. Measuring sliding friction.

means of a cord, attach the hook of the balance to the screw eye in the end of the box (Fig. 7–1). Holding the spring balance horizontally, find how many grams' pull are required to start the box sliding and how many to keep it moving slowly and steadily along the board. The box will stick a little in places where the friction is greatest. Therefore several trials should be made and the average taken as the friction resistance. It is easier to read the balance if the board is drawn under the box than if the box is pulled over the board.

By loading the box with weights, it is possible to get any desired pressure between the bearing surfaces. It is well to start with as small a load as will give a fairly steady reading on the spring balance. Then increase the load and make five trials, using widely varying loads up to the capacity of the balance. Compute in each trial the coefficient of sliding friction expressed as a decimal and then the average coefficient of sliding friction for leather on wood.

Record the data and results in tabular form:

TRIALS	I	II	III	IV	V
Weight of empty box .					
Load					
Weight of box and load					
Starting friction . . .					
Sliding friction					
Coefficient of sliding friction					

* * * *

On an inclined plane. Raise one end of the board until the loaded box, once started, will slowly slide down the board with a uniform velocity. Then, keeping the board in this position, measure the vertical distance H from the under side of the raised end to the table and the horizontal distance B from the foot of this vertical line to the point where the lower end of the board rests on the table (Fig. 7–2).

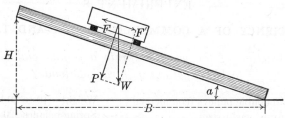

Fig. 7–2. Friction on an incline.

Change the weights in the box and in each trial adjust the height so that the box will only just continue to slide after it is once started by hand.

In each trial compute the ratio of the vertical distance to the horizontal and express the result as a decimal fraction.* Record the data and computed results as on the next page.

* The grade of a state highway is usually given as a number of feet rise per hundred feet of length (horizontal).

	VERTICAL DISTANCE (H)	HORIZONTAL DISTANCE (B)	H/B
Box lightly loaded	cm.	cm.	
Box with added weight . . .			
Box heavily loaded			

Conclusions. Answer the following questions in complete sentences.

(a) *Is the starting friction in each trial greater than the sliding friction?*

(b) *Does the sliding friction increase with the pressure?*

(c) *Does the coefficient of sliding friction increase with the pressure?*

(d) *Does the numerical value obtained by dividing the vertical distance by the horizontal approximately equal the coefficient of sliding friction?* *

EXPERIMENT 8

EFFICIENCY OF A COMMERCIAL BLOCK AND TACKLE

What fraction of the work put into a commercial block and tackle is got out with various loads?

Two double pulleys (commercial form, yacht size)
Rope

Weights (10 to 50 lbs.)
Spring balance (20 lbs.)
Meter stick

Introduction. In any commercial machine the work done by the machine in lifting a weight or overcoming a resistance is always less than the work expended on or put into the machine.   To be efficient a machine must return as useful work a large part of the work applied to it.   The mechanical efficiency of a machine is the ratio of the output to the input.

* For the geometrical proof of this conclusion, study page 179 in BLACK AND DAVIS' *Elementary Practical Physics*.

The ratio is always less than one, and it is usually expressed as a percentage. Thus,

$$\text{Efficiency} = \frac{\text{output}}{\text{input}} = \frac{\text{work done by machine}}{\text{work done on machine}}$$

Output = efficiency × input.

One of the simplest machines to use to illustrate the meaning of efficiency is the commercial block and tackle, which consists of a combination of pulleys connected by a rope. One block, called the *fixed* block, is fastened to a hook in the ceiling or to a bracket on the wall. The other block, known as the *movable* block, is attached to the load to be lifted. It will be noted that the movable block is the one that moves up and down with the weight.

We shall find it helpful to compute the **velocity ratio** of the block and tackle, which is the ratio obtained by dividing the distance through which the driving force (effort) acts by the distance through which the resisting force (load) acts in the same time. We can easily compute this velocity ratio by counting the number of supporting strands. For example, in the apparatus shown in figure 8–1 there are four strands supporting the movable pulley. Therefore the velocity ratio is four. This means that to raise the weight 1 foot the effort acts through a distance of 4 feet.

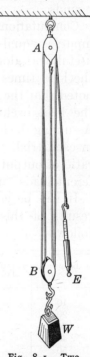

Fig. 8–1. Two double blocks.

Directions. Attach one block A to a ring in the ceiling or to a suitable bracket from the wall. Hang a weight W on the lower block B. Determine by means of a spring balance the effort E required to raise the load slowly and steadily. Note the zero error of the spring balance when used in this position, and make the proper correction for this zero error.

Determine by actual measurement the distance through which the effort must be exerted in order to lift the weight 1 foot. Compare this value of the velocity ratio with that which you would expect from the arrangement of ropes and pulleys.

Make several trials, using weights of 10, 20, 30, and 50 pounds.

Computations. The work done by the effort, that is, the input, is equal to the effort times the effort distance. The useful work done on the load, that is, the output, is equal to the load times the distance the load is lifted. It is to be noted that the useful output means the work done in lifting the load exclusive of the weight of the movable block. Assuming the load is raised 1 foot, calculate output and input in each trial. Finally, compute the efficiency, that is, the ratio of output to input, of the block and tackle at the different loads, and express this efficiency as per cent.

It will be convenient to record the data and computed results of this experiment in tabular form somewhat as follows :

LOAD IN POUNDS	EFFORT IN POUNDS	VELOCITY RATIO	OUTPUT IN FOOT-POUNDS	INPUT IN FOOT-POUNDS	EFFICIENCY IN PER CENT
10		4			
20		4			
30		4			
40		4			
50		4			

* * * *

Results. If time permits, it will be interesting to plot the results of this experiment as two curves showing graphically the relation of the *effort* to the *load* and the relation of the *efficiency* to the *load*. It is customary to plot the loads along the "x," or horizontal, axis and the efforts and efficiencies along the "y," or vertical, axis.*

Figure 8–2 shows a graph which is typical for many machines. It will be noticed that the effort-load curve starts a little above zero as some effort is required to drive the

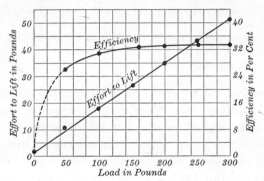

Fig. 8–2. Curves of a differential chain block.

machine unloaded. The efficiency curve always starts at zero since the efficiency at no load must necessarily be zero.

(a) *How does the effort applied to a commercial block and tackle vary with the load?*

(b) *Is the efficiency of a block and tackle the same with different loads?*

(c) *What becomes of the "wasted work"?*

* For further information in regard to plotting curves see Appendix.

EFFICIENCY OF A COMMERCIAL JACKSCREW

What is the velocity ratio and what is the efficiency of a commercial jackscrew under varying loads?

Commercial jackscrew	Spring balance (20 lbs.)
A 4-foot lever arm	Yardstick
Anchorage bar	

Introduction. Jackscrews have long been used by builders to raise buildings from their foundations. A small force applied to the end of an iron bar which is used to turn the screw causes the screw to exert an enormous upward force through a very short distance. In one complete revolution of the handle the load is lifted the distance between two adjacent threads (*pitch of the screw*). The extensive use of automobiles has made many of us acquainted with the automobile jackscrew. In one form, the effort is applied to the handle and is then transmitted through a bevel gear to a nut, which turns and lifts the screw.

In order to get a sufficient load to test the jackscrew under conditions which approach actual working conditions, the jack is placed under a lever a short distance from the fulcrum F, as shown in figure 8-3. By this arrangement the total load to be lifted can readily be computed from the principle of moments. Consider the effect of the weight of the lever which acts at its center of gravity and of the weight or pull P which is exerted at the opposite end from the fulcrum. Then compute the sum of the moments about F tending to turn the lever clockwise, and make this equal to the moment of the upward push W of the jackscrew against the beam.

The velocity ratio of the jackscrew can be computed from the circumference of the circle through which the effort E

moves and from the distance the load is lifted, that is, the pitch of the screw. Both distances must be expressed in the same unit.

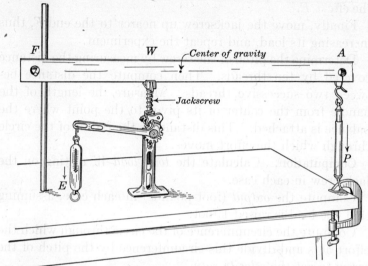

Fig. 8–3. Testing a jackscrew by means of a lever.

The efficiency of the jackscrew can be obtained by computing the output, that is, the work done in lifting the total load on the screw a unit distance, say 1 foot, and the input, or the work done by the effort required to lift this load 1 foot. The output in foot-pounds is then equal numerically to the load expressed in pounds, and the input in foot-pounds is equal to the effort times the velocity ratio. The efficiency is equal to the output divided by the input, and the decimal fraction is expressed as per cent.

Directions. The weight of the beam and the position of its center of gravity have been marked on it. Set up the apparatus as shown in figure 8–3, and level the beam by means of the clamp at F. Suspend a 50-pound weight or attach a spring balance at A. Measure the effort with a 20-pound spring balance E attached to the end of the handle.

Read the balance when it is acting at right angles to the handle and moving slowly.

Then increase the suspended load or pull P and measure the effort E.

Finally, move the jackscrew up nearer to the end F, thus increasing its load, and repeat the experiment.

Determine the pitch of the screw by measuring the distance covered by ten threads. Then compute the distance between two successive threads. Measure the length of the handle from the center of its pivot to the point where the balance is attached. This distance is the radius of the circle through which the effort moves.

Computation. Calculate the *total load* W resting on the jackscrew in each case.

Compute the *output* (foot-pounds) in each case, assuming that the load is raised 1 foot.

Compute the circumference of the circle through which the effort acts and divide this circumference by the pitch of the screw to get the *velocity ratio*.

Then the *input* will be equal to the effort times the velocity ratio.

Finally, the *efficiency* is computed in each case as the ratio of the output to the input and expressed as per cent.

*   *   *   *

Results. If time permits, the results of this experiment may well be expressed graphically by plotting two curves, one to show the relation of the effort to the load and the other to show the relation of the efficiency to the load. It is customary to plot the loads horizontally and the efforts and efficiencies vertically as shown in figure 8–2.

EXPERIMENT 9

MEASURING ONE'S HORSEPOWER

(a) *How much power do you use in running upstairs?*
(b) *How much power do you use in turning a crank?*

Meter stick with inches on the other side
Stop watch to $\frac{1}{5}$ sec.
Balance, personal-weight scale

Crank and friction axle (Miller * form)
Spring balance (30 lbs.)

Introduction. It is an interesting fact that the world had no unit of power (rate of doing work) until the development of the steam engine by James Watt. Since he was trying to displace the horse with his machine, he measured the power of a very strong dray horse and found it could work at the rate of 33,000 foot-pounds per minute. He was quite aware of the fact that this rate is for a strong horse during a short time only. Of course this does not mean that any horse, by means of a rope and pulley, can lift 33,000 pounds one foot in one minute, but simply that the product of the force in pounds times the distance in feet which it moves in one minute is 33,000. It is sometimes more convenient to divide this by 60 and get 550 foot-pounds per second.

Directions. It will be more interesting to take a stairway with two or three flights of stairs running continuously upward. If one runs upstairs, he does work in lifting his own weight through a vertical height. If we measure the time it takes to run upstairs, we can easily compute the foot-pounds of work done per second and then the horsepower.

The first step is to determine one's weight to the nearest half-pound on a balance (such as is commonly used in a

---

* This apparatus was devised by Mr. Fred R. Miller of the English High School, Boston, Mass.

43

bathroom). Then, to get the vertical height, we have merely to measure to $\frac{1}{16}$ of an inch the rise in one step and count the number of steps. In this way we can compute the vertical height of the flight of stairs. To get the time (seconds) required to run up the stairs will require several trials. It is well to let one person do the running upstairs while another with a stop watch measures to $\frac{1}{5}$ of a second the actual time required to run up one flight of stairs and then the time required to run up *two* flights, one immediately after the other. Record these data in tabular form.

Data

Weight (W) . . . . lbs.

Rise of each step (h) . . . . in.

Number of steps in flight (n) . . . .

Time to run up one flight of stairs (t) . . . . sec.

Time to run up two flights (t') . . . . sec.

Computations

Total height of stairs in flight (H) . . . . ft.

Work done in running up one flight of stairs (WH) . . ft.-lbs.

Work done per second $\left(\dfrac{WH}{t}\right)$ . . . . ft.-lbs./sec.

Horsepower $\left(\dfrac{WH}{550\,t}\right)$ . . . .

Total height of two flights (H') . . . . ft.

Work done in running up two flights (WH') . . . . . ft.-lbs.

Work done per second $\left(\dfrac{WH'}{t'}\right)$ . . . . ft.-lbs./sec.

Horsepower developed $\left(\dfrac{WH'}{550\,t'}\right)$ . . . .

Results. *State exactly the distinction between work and power. Define the unit of power. Was the result of this experiment more or less than expected? Why? Why is the power less in going up two flights than in one flight?*

* * * *

Measuring horsepower with a crank. If time permits, measure your power by turning a crank against friction

applied at the axle, as shown in figure 9–1. By tightening
up the wing nut *W* on the wooden frame *C*, we can exert
considerable friction on the axle *D*. With a suitable spring
balance (30 lbs.) attached to the handle of the crank, we

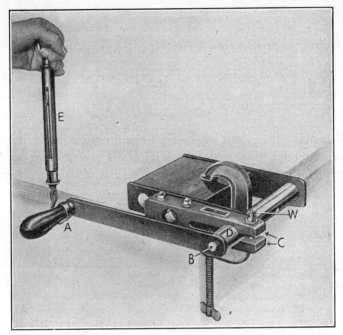

Fig. 9-1. Measuring your power by turning the crank against friction.

can measure the pull, or force, *E* required to turn the crank.
It must be observed that this pull is exerted at right angles
to the crank arm *AB*. Now if we turn the crank for just
a minute and count the number of revolutions (r.p.m.),
we can compute the work done in one minute, that is, the
force (lbs.) times the circumference in feet ($2\pi r$) times the
revolutions per minute. Then we can compute the horsepower from the following equation:

$$\text{H.P.} = \frac{\text{foot-pounds per minute}}{33,000}.$$

Data

Radius of crank AB (R) . . . . in.

Force required to turn crank (E) . . . . lbs.

Revolutions per minute (r.p.m.) . . . .

Computation

Circumference described by crank $\left(\dfrac{2\,\pi R}{12}\right)$ . . . ft.

Work done in one revolution $\left(\dfrac{2\,\pi RE}{12}\right)$. . . . . ft.-lbs.

Horsepower developed $\left(\dfrac{2\,\pi RE}{12 \times 33,000}\right)$. . . . .

Results. *Why is it necessary to pull on the crank handle at right angles to the crank? Why is the power developed in turning the crank not the same as that used in running upstairs? Could you work at this rate all day?*

MECHANICS (*continued*)

BLOCK II. MECHANICS OF FLUIDS. PROPERTIES OF MATTER

Suggestive Questions

1. Why does an iron anchor sink and an iron ship *float*?
2. How could you check the readings of a battery hydrometer?
3. Would an inflated inner tube of an automobile tire serve as a life preserver?
4. Why is a stone apparently lighter under water than in air?
5. Does the lifting effect of water on an anchor depend upon its depth below the surface?
6. How could you weigh a cubic foot of the air in this room?
7. Does Archimedes' principle apply to gases?
8. What property of air is utilized in pneumatic tires?
9. If two steel cables will support an elevator car, why use four?
10. What law of physics is illustrated in a letter balance?
11. If the atmosphere presses on all sides of a balloon, why does *it* rise?
12. What is meant by "priming the pump" to start it?
13. How is compressed air used in a rural water system?
14. How is the tube in a barometer filled with mercury?
15. How can you pump water from an artesian well which is 100 feet deep?
16. When an automobile is raised by an hydraulic lift, does the required pressure depend upon the height to which it is raised?

EXPERIMENT 10

BUOYANCY OF LIQUIDS — ARCHIMEDES' PRINCIPLE

How much does a body lose in apparent weight when entirely immersed in a liquid?

Solids denser than water (150–250 g.), such as stone, coal, glass, block of lignum vitae, etc.
Platform balance with weights and support, or a spring balance (250 g.) *

Overflow can
Catch bucket or beaker with wire loop for suspension
Jar of water and thread

Introduction. It is common experience that one can lift a much heavier stone to the surface of a pond than one can lift out of the water. The anchor of a boat seems to be much heavier when it is out of water than when it is in water. A submarine boat may float partly submerged or sink to any depth, as conditions may require. What is it that determines whether a thing sinks or floats in a liquid?

It is obvious that any object when submerged displaces a *volume* of liquid equal to the *volume* of the object itself. It will be interesting to compare the *weight* of the liquid displaced with the loss in weight of a body either partly or wholly submerged in a liquid.

This buoyant action of water was probably first studied about 240 B.C. by Archimedes, and therefore the principle involved is known as Archimedes' principle.

---

* If a spring balance is used in this experiment, each of the weights will be in error by 1 or 2 grams and consequently the results will not agree precisely with the principle involved.

48

Directions. *Solids that sink.* First weigh the specimen, such as a piece of stone, *in air* and then when entirely *immersed in water* in a jar. Compute the loss in apparent weight.

To determine the weight of the liquid displaced, a can with a spout, called an overflow can (Fig. 10–1), is filled until the water runs out at the spout. Then, by placing a weighed catch bucket under the spout and carefully lowering the piece of rock into the overflow can, the water which is displaced overflows into the bucket, where it is caught and weighed.

If time permits, repeat the experiment, using gasoline as the liquid instead of water.

Record your observations and results as follows:

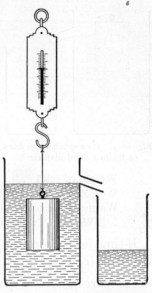

Fig. 10–1. How much weight does the solid appear to lose?

LIQUIDS USED	WATER	GASOLINE
Weight of solid in air	g.	g.
Weight of solid in liquid	g.	g.
Loss of weight in liquid	g.	g.
Weight of catch bucket, empty :	g.	g.
Weight of catch bucket and liquid displaced .	g.	g.
Weight of liquid displaced	g.	g.

Compare the loss in weight of the stone in a liquid with the weight of the liquid displaced.

* * * *

Solids that float. A solid which is lighter than water loses its entire weight, and therefore we should expect it to sink into the water until it displaced its own weight of water. To find out how the weight of a floating body compares

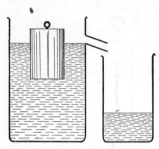

Fig. 10–2.   How much water does a floating solid displace?

with the weight of the liquid displaced by it, first weigh the object, such as a block of wood or an apple; then arrange the overflow can and catch bucket as shown in figure 10–2 and determine the weight of water displaced by the floating object.

Record these observations and results as follows:

Weight of solid . . . . g.
Weight of catch bucket, empty . . . . g.
Weight of catch bucket and water displaced   . . . .   g.
Weight of water displaced . . . .   g.

If time permits, repeat the experiment using gasoline as the liquid instead of water.

Compare the weight of a floating object with the weight of the liquid displaced by it.

EXPERIMENT 11

SPECIFIC GRAVITY OF SOLIDS

How many times is a given solid as heavy as an equal volume of water?

Heavy solids (100–250 g.), such as pieces of marble, glass, metal, sulfur, etc.	Platform balance with set of weights and support, or spring balance (250 g.)
Light solids, such as cork, wood, paraffin, etc.	Lead sinker
	Jar of water and thread

Introduction. The specific gravity of a substance is one of its most important characteristics. For example, the specific gravity of lead is 11.4; this means that lead is 11.4 times as heavy as an equal bulk of water. The specific gravity of a substance is a pure number and is always the same, irrespective of the unit of weight used. To determine the specific gravity of a solid, we first weigh the object, next find the weight of an equal bulk of water, and finally divide the weight of the object by the weight of an equal bulk of water. In other words,

$$\text{Specific gravity} = \frac{\text{weight of body}}{\text{weight of equal bulk of water}}.$$

In the case of a regular geometrical solid, we can measure the dimensions, calculate the volume, and from the latter get the weight of an equal bulk of water. (See Experiment 2.)

If the solid is irregular and will sink in water, we can apply the principle of Archimedes and determine its apparent loss of weight in water. This is the weight of an equal bulk of water.

If the solid is irregular and lighter than water, we can determine the weight of an equal bulk of water by means of a sinker suspended below the object. First get the weight of the solid in air with the sinker attached and under water. Then weigh *both* the solid and sinker submerged in water. This

51

weight will be less than the first, for the water buoys up the object. The difference between the two weights is equal to the weight of the water displaced by the object.

Thus it will be seen that the various methods of finding the specific gravity of solids vary only in the manner in which the weight of an equal bulk of water is found.

Directions. *Solids which sink in water.* Weigh the specimen of rock, metal, or sulfur in the usual way. Then suspend the object by a thread and weigh the solid entirely submerged in water, taking care that the specimen does

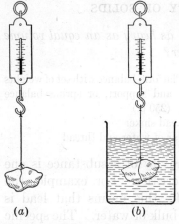

(a)   (b)

Fig. 11–1. Weight in air (a) and weight in water (b). How great is the difference?

not touch the sides or bottom of the jar (Fig. 11–1). Air bubbles are liable to adhere to the body when submerged in water and increase the displacement. Therefore it is well to remove them as far as possible by lifting the solid up out of the water for an instant.

Record your observations and results in tabular form:

SUBSTANCES USED	GLASS	COAL	SULFUR
Weight of solid in air			
Weight of solid in water			
Loss of weight in water			
Weight of equal volume of water			
Specific gravity of solid			

Compare your values for the specific gravity of the substances tested with those given in the TABLE OF DENSITIES (III) *in the Appendix. Account for the general agree-*

*ment between the specific gravity as found by experiment and
the densities as given in grams per cubic centimeter. How do
you account for the differences?*

If spring balances are used in this experiment, the weights
will be easily determined, but only very roughly. If platform balances are used, the scales must be supported a
foot or more above the table, and the object can be suspended
by a thread directly under one platform. When a beam
balance is used, a special device is usually provided for this
experiment.

*   *   *   *

Solids lighter than water. First weigh the block of wood
or paraffin alone in air. Then weigh the block in air with the
sinker attached and in water, as shown in figure 11–2 a. (It

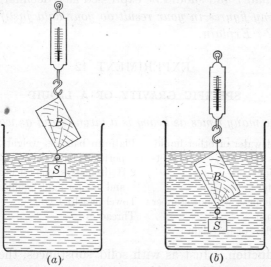

(a)   (b)

Fig. 11–2. (a) Weighing the block *B* in air and the sinker *S* in water; (b) block and
sinker both under water. What causes the difference?

may be more convenient to weigh the sinker alone under
water and add this to the weight of the block in air.) Finally,
weigh both block and sinker submerged in water, as shown
in figure 11–2 b. The difference between the third and the

second weights is obviously due to the buoyant action of the water on the block alone, and this is equal to the weight of the water displaced by the block. From this difference and the weight of the block in air, obtain the specific gravity of the block used in this experiment.

Arrange your data and results as follows:

Weight of block of —— in air . . . . g.
Weight of sinker in water . . . . g.
Weight of block in air and sinker in water . . . . g.
Weight of block and sinker *both* in water. . . . . g.
   Lifting effect of water on block . . . . g.
Specific gravity of block . . . .

Since the solid is lighter than water, its specific gravity will be less than 1 and should be expressed as a decimal fraction. *How many figures in your result do your data justify you in keeping? Explain.*

EXPERIMENT 12

SPECIFIC GRAVITY OF A LIQUID

How many times as heavy is a given liquid as water?

Jar of salt water or other liquid, such as kerosene, carbon tetrachloride
Jar of water
Volumetric flask without stopper (250 cm.³)
Piece of glass or porcelain
Platform balance, weights, and support, or spring balance (250 g.)
2 Hydrometers, one for heavy liquids and one for light liquids
Towel (crash) 1 yd.²
Thread

Introduction. Just as with solid substances, the specific gravity of a liquid is one of its most important characteristics. For example, if the specific gravity of the acid solution in a lead storage battery is 1.30, we know that the battery is fully charged; whereas if its specific gravity is only 1.15, we know that the battery is nearly discharged and should be recharged immediately. Again, suppose we test the mixture of denatured alcohol and water in an automobile radiator and find its specific gravity to be 0.933. We can tell by tables that its freezing point is − 32° F. If, on the other hand, its specific gravity were 0.975, its freezing point would be 14° F.

To find the specific gravity of a liquid (or solid), we divide the weight of a given specimen by the weight of an equal volume of water. One method is to use a graduated glass flask to get equal volumes of the liquid to be tested and of water, and then to compare the weight of the liquid in the

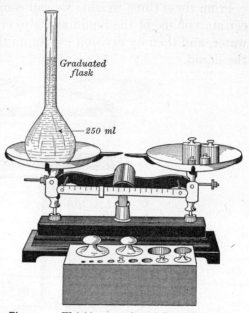

Graduated flask

250 ml

Fig. 12–1. Weighing a graduated flask filled to the mark.

flask with the weight of the same volume of water. Another method is to weigh some object, like a piece of glass, in air, in the given liquid, and in water, and then to compare the loss of weight in the liquid with the loss of weight in water. The commercial method is to float a suitable hydrometer in the given liquid and to read the specific gravity directly by noting the position on the scale in the stem of the surface of the liquid.

Directions. I. *Bottle method.* First find the weight of the empty (dry) flask; then find the weight of the flask filled with the liquid to be tested up to the mark on the neck (Fig. 12–1). Finally, find the weight of the same flask filled with water up to the same mark. It is necessary, of course, to wipe the outside of the flask dry each time.

From these three weights we can compute the weight of a certain volume of the liquid and also of the same volume of water, and then by division we obtain the specific gravity of the liquid.

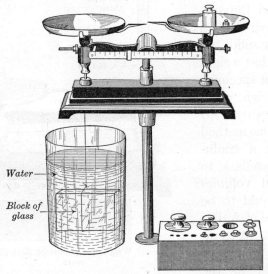

Water—

Block of glass

Fig. 12–2. Weighing a glass block in a liquid.

Record the weighings and computed results as follows :

Weight of empty flask . . . . g.
Weight of flask and liquid . . . . g.
Weight of flask and water . . . . g.
Weight of liquid in flask . . . . g.
Weight of water in flask . . . . g.
Specific gravity of liquid . . . .

II. *Displacement method.* Weigh some object, such as a piece of glass or porcelain, in air ; then weigh the same object submerged in the liquid to be tested, and again weigh the object submerged in water. A platform balance when properly supported in an elevated position (Fig. 12–2) or a beam balance with some special device for weighing objects submerged in a liquid will give much more accurate results than the ordinary spring balance. Be sure that the object when weighed in the submerged condition does not touch the bottom or sides of the jar and is fairly free from air bubbles.

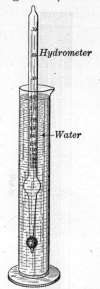

Fig. 12–3. Hydrometer.

From these three weights compute the loss of weight in the liquid; that is, according to the principle of Archimedes, the weight of the liquid displaced. In the same way compute the loss of weight in water, which is the weight of an equal volume of water. Finally, by comparing these *losses in weight* in the liquid and in water, determine the specific gravity of the liquid.

Record the weighings and computed results as follows:

Weight of piece of glass in air . . . . g.
Weight of piece of glass in liquid . . . . g.
Weight of piece of glass in water . . . . g.
Loss of weight in liquid . . . . g.
Loss of weight in water . . . . g.
Specific gravity of liquid . . . .

III. *Hydrometer method.* Fill a tall jar nearly full of the liquid to be tested and float the hydrometer in the liquid (Fig. 12–3). Read the position of the surface of the liquid on the hydrometer scale and thus get the specific gravity directly.

*   *   *   *

Balancing columns. A very rapid and precise method of comparing the density of a liquid with that of water, that is, determining the specific gravity of a liquid, is to balance

a column of the liquid with a column of water, as shown in
figure 12–4. If we draw some of the air out of the tube

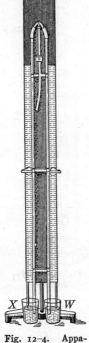

and then close the screw pinchcock, it is
evident that the pressure of the air on the
liquids in the tumblers is holding up the two
columns. Both liquid columns exert at their
bases the same pressure, which depends on
the height and density of the liquid. Consequently the liquid of less density will have
the greater height, and the densities of the
two liquids X and W vary *inversely* as the
lengths of their columns. From this it follows that

$$\left. \begin{array}{l} \text{Specific gravity} \\ \text{of liquid} \end{array} \right\} = \frac{\text{density of liquid}}{\text{density of water}}$$

$$= \frac{\text{length of water column}}{\text{length of liquid column}}.$$

Set up the apparatus and make three
determinations of the specific gravity of some
liquid, such as kerosene, by balancing columns.

Repeat using another liquid, such as alcohol, milk, carbon tetrachloride, or turpentine.
Now balance the second liquid used against

Fig. 12–4. Appa-
ratus for balanc-
ing columns of
two liquids.

the kerosene. How does the ratio of the lengths of the
columns compare with the densities just found in the first
part of this experiment?

EXPERIMENT 13

THE MERCURY BAROMETER

What are the principles involved in the construction and use of the mercury barometer?

Wide-mouthed bottle (8 oz.) fitted with 2-hole rubber stopper
Barometer tube, 38 inches long, open at both ends, with a stopcock near the upper end, mounted on a stand
Glass L-tube
Mercury (2 lbs.), redistilled
Rubber tubing with screw pinchcock
Meter stick
Air pumps, pressure and vacuum

Introduction. Probably we all know that a barometer is used to predict the weather and to measure altitudes. But perhaps we do not know that the mercury barometer is standard and is used to mark the scale on metallic barometers. How is it made and how does it work? We may easily answer these questions and many others about the barometer by setting up the experimental apparatus * shown in figure 13–1. With this apparatus we shall be able to measure the pressure of the atmosphere and to see how atmospheric pressure varies with the weather and with the altitude.

Directions. I. Set up the apparatus as shown in figure 13–1. Open both stopcocks and with the pressure pump force air into the bottle until the

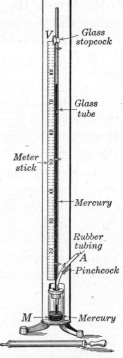

Fig. 13–1. **Experimental barometer.**

* This form of apparatus was suggested by Mr. John C. Packard, High School, Brookline, Mass.

mercury rises in the long tube just above its stopcock. Close this cock and remove the pump. Make a diagram of the apparatus.

(1) *Why does the mercury rise in the tube?*

(2) *How high (centimeters) is the mercury in the tube above that in the bottle?*

(3) *What is above the mercury in the tube?*

(4) *If the column of mercury were one square centimeter in cross section, how many grams would this column of mercury weigh?*

(5) *How much pressure must the air exert on the mercury in the bottle to hold up this column of mercury?*

II. Attach the vacuum pump to the short tube and reduce the pressure of the air on the mercury in the bottle.

(1) *Why does the mercury in the long tube go down?*

(2) *How can you measure the pressure of the air left in the bottle?*

III. Open the stopcock in the long tube and attach the vacuum pump to this tube. Exhaust the air from the tube slowly and steadily as much as the pump will permit. Close the upper stopcock.

(1) *Why does the mercury rise in the long tube?*

(2) *Why does it not rise as high as in I?*

(3) *What fraction of the air has been removed from the tube by the pump?*

In answering the above questions, make complete statements and refer to the diagram of the apparatus which you have drawn in your notebook.

* * * *

Pressure gauges. Repeat this experiment with a Bourdon pressure and vacuum gauge connected between the pump and the apparatus. Compare the gauge readings with the heights of the mercury in the tube.

Set up a mercury barometer essentially as in I and record its readings together with weather conditions every day for two weeks. What kind of weather usually follows or accompanies "low" barometric pressure? Learn to adjust and read a standard mercury barometer.

EXPERIMENT 14

DENSITY OF AIR

What is the weight of a liter of air under the conditions of temperature and pressure of the room?

Two-liter round-bottom flask, with 1-hole rubber stopper and tubing, extra thick wall
Vacuum pump and mercury gauge
Barometer

2 Screw pinchcocks
Y-tube
Equal-arm balance sensitive to 0.05 g.
Set of weights

Introduction. When riding fast we feel the air although we cannot see it. We have just learned how we may measure the pressure of the atmosphere about us by means of a barometer. When a barometer is carried up into the air above the surface of the earth, as in an airplane, we find that the pressure decreases. These facts indicate that we are living at the bottom of an ocean of air.

Since air is a substance which occupies space, it must have weight. Ordinarily we are not conscious of any pressure due to its weight because it is a gas and is all around and within us. The problem of determining the weight of a definite volume of air and then computing the weight in grams of one liter of air is the same in principle as that of finding the density of any substance (see Exp. 2), but the experiment requires more precautions. First, air is so light a substance that we must use a sensitive balance. Second, to determine the volume of the air, we use a 2-liter flask and weigh it with air and without. But we can never quite exhaust the flask and so must measure with a mercury gauge the fraction of the air removed. Everything considered, the problem of finding the density of air will challenge our patience and skill.

Directions. First of all it is assumed that the **volume of the flask** has already been determined by filling it with water and then measuring the volume of water with a graduate.

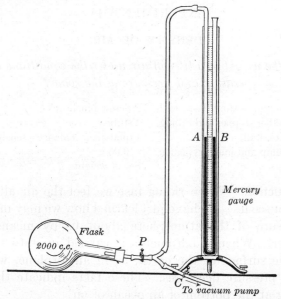

Fig. 14–1. How much air can we pump out of this flask?

When this volume has once been determined, it is marked on a label on the flask, and this part of the experiment need not be repeated; but great care should be taken to have the flask dry and clean both inside and out.

Connect the flask, mercury gauge, and vacuum pump as shown in figure 14–1. Pump out some of the air, close the rubber tube connected with the pump by means of pinchcock *C*, and watch the mercury gauge to see whether there is a leak in the connections. A gradual drop of the mercury would indicate such a leak, which must be stopped before proceeding. When all the connections are tight, continue pumping for at least five minutes and then *read the mercury gauge* (*i.e.*, height of mercury in tube *A* above that in tube *B*). Close tightly the pinchcock *P* near the flask.

Disconnect the flask with its tube and pinchcock, suspend it from one arm of the balance, and counterpoise its weight with great care. Without disturbing the flask or balance, open the pinchcock and let the air in. Add the necessary weights to make up for the air admitted. This added weight represents the **weight of air** admitted to the flask.

Computations. But not quite all the air was removed from the flask by the pump. In fact, only that *fraction of the total volume of the flask* indicated by the height of mercury in the pressure gauge divided by the height of mercury in the barometer was removed.

Having calculated, then, the number of cubic centimeters of air admitted and its weight, we may readily compute the weight of 1000 cubic centimeters.

Since the weight of air varies greatly with the temperature and pressure, it is well to record the room temperature and barometric pressure and then check the experimental result of this rather crude method with the results given in the tables in the Appendix.

Arrange the data and calculated results in an orderly fashion and draw a labeled diagram of the apparatus.

* * * *

Another method.* Into a strong metal can (of about 1-liter capacity) we pump air with a compression pump. After from 40 to 50 strokes, we close the needle valve in the top of the can and weigh the can on a beam balance to 0.01 gram (Fig. 14–2). Then we attach a rubber tube

---

* This method was suggested by Mr. J. Hawley Aiken of the Technical High School, Springfield, Mass.

to the valve-stem and collect the excess air (which is about 3000 cm.³) in a large graduated cylinder by displacement of water over a pneumatic trough. We shall have to repeat this process several times in order to collect all the air which

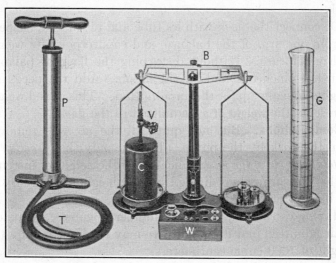

Fig. 14-2. Density of air by weighing the can C filled with compressed air.

has been forced into the can. Record the *total volume* of air thus collected and reweigh the can. The difference in weight of the can gives the *weight of the air*. Compute the density of air in grams per liter at the temperature and pressure of the room.

Compare your value for the density of air with that given in Table IV (Appendix) and compute the percentage error. What are the most probable sources of error in this experiment?

EXPERIMENT 15

COMPRESSIBILITY OF AIR — BOYLE'S LAW

How does the volume of a given quantity of air kept at constant temperature vary with the pressure?

Boyle's Law apparatus with two adjustable glass tubes connected by rubber tubing and mounted on some convenient upright rod. (One tube, 30 cm.³, graduated to 0.1 cm.³ and provided with glass stopcock.)

Barometer
Millimeter cross-section paper
Meter stick

Introduction. With an ordinary compression pump we can force air into an automobile tire until the desired pressure (indicated by a gauge) is obtained. How much air at ordinary pressure has been forced into the tube to produce this pressure? If we knew this volume of air and the dimensions of the pump, then we could compute the number of strokes required. But this assumes that the pump is perfect and does not leak, and of course that is not the case with any practical pump. By comparing, however, this theoretical number of strokes with the actual number of strokes required to produce a given pressure, we can compute the efficiency of the compression pump.

But all problems which have to do with the compressibility of gases depend upon a very important principle relating to the volume and pressure of a given quantity of a gas at constant temperature. This was discovered about 1662 by Robert Boyle. It will greatly help us to understand the meaning of this principle if we ourselves repeat his "experiments touching the spring of the air."

Directions. A convenient form of apparatus for observing the effect of varying pressures in changing the volume of a given quantity of air is the apparatus shown in figure 15–1. It consists of two glass tubes connected by a rubber tube which is securely wired to the glass tubes. These glass tubes are clamped in a vertical position. The tube on the right is provided with a glass stopcock and graduated into cubic centimeters and tenths of cubic centimeters. When the stopcock is open, the mercury stands at the same level in both tubes. Adjust the tubes so that you have about 20 cubic centimeters of air in the right tube and then close the stopcock and keep it closed during the experiment. Why?

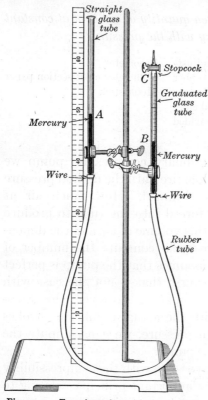

Fig. 15–1. Experimenting with the elasticity of air.

To determine the pressure we note that the air is pressing on the mercury in the open tube (left) and that this atmospheric pressure is equivalent to the pressure of the column of mercury in the barometer. If the mercury stands at the same level in both tubes, then the pressure P exerted on the column of air is the atmospheric pressure and is obtained by reading the barometer expressed in centimeters. If the mercury in the open tube stands at a lower level than that in the closed tube, then the air in the tube is under less than atmospheric pressure, and the pressure is equal to the barometric pressure *minus* the difference in levels, both expressed in centimeters. But if the level of the mercury in the open arm is higher than it is in the closed arm, then the air is under more than atmospheric pressure and the pressure is equal to the barometric pressure *plus* the difference in levels.

By raising the open tube (left), it is possible to increase the pressure P on the enclosed air from one atmosphere to two atmospheres and to observe the resulting changes in the volume V of the air in the tube. By lowering the open tube, we may decrease the pressure P on the closed air below one atmosphere. Since the volume of a gas is very sensitive to changes in temperature, it is well not to handle the air column with warm hands. In reading the position of the mercury on the meter stick, be sure that your eye is on a level with the mercury and that you always read the top of the mercury surface.

Record the reading of the barometer at the time of the experiment. Record also the positions of the mercury-surface in the closed arm B and in the open arm A. Change the positions of the tubes so as to change the pressure on the air in the closed tube. Continue this process of changing the pressure and reading the levels until the volume of the air is compressed to about one half of its original volume.

Record your readings and computed results in tabular form as follows, keeping only significant figures in the last column:

Atmospheric pressure (barometer) . . . . cm.

POSITION OF MERCURY IN OPEN TUBE (A)	POSITION OF MERCURY IN CLOSED TUBE (B)	DIFFERENCE IN MERCURY LEVELS	TOTAL PRESSURE P	VOLUME OF AIR V	PRESSURE TIMES VOLUME P × V
cm.	cm.	cm.	cm.	cm.^{3}	

Results. By comparing the values obtained in this experiment for the total pressure P and for the volume of the air V, it will be evident that when the *pressure increases* the *volume decreases*. But this relation may be expressed more precisely. If we multiply in each trial the total pressure by the corresponding volume, we find that the resulting products PV are nearly **constant.** In other words,

$$P_1 \times V_1 = P_2 \times V_2 = P_3 \times V_3, \text{ or } \frac{V_1}{V_2} = \frac{P_2}{P_1} \text{ and } \frac{V_2}{V_3} = \frac{P_3}{P_2}.$$

In general, then, we find that the volume of the air in the tube varies *inversely* as the pressure. This means that when the pressure is doubled the volume is halved provided that the temperature remains constant and none of the air escapes.

* * * *

Graphical representations of results. If we compute the average value of PV, we can, by using this constant, find the pressures which would correspond to two, three, and four times the greatest observed volume. In the same way we can find the volumes which would correspond to two, three, and four times the greatest measured pressure.

Plot these six pressures with their corresponding volumes and also the observed pressures and volumes. Represent the pressures as vertical distances and the volumes as horizontal distances. Draw a smooth curve through these points, using a solid line through the observed points and a dashed line through the six computed points.* Note that this curve, if continued, would come very close to, but never quite touch, the axes. Such a curve is called a **hyperbola.**

Other forms of apparatus. Perhaps the simplest form of apparatus for studying the effect of varying pressures on the volume of a given quantity of air at some fixed temperature is the **J-tube** (Fig. 15–2), which was the form

---

* For further suggestions about plotting curves, see Appendix.

used by Boyle. The short arm BC is closed at the top C and is assumed to be of uniform cross section so that the volume of the air enclosed within will vary as the length of the air column. We first carefully pour a little mercury into the tube until the mercury covers the bend. We may now tip the tube so as to allow air to escape from the short tube until the mercury stands at the same height in both tubes. Then we read and record the positions of C, B, and A. The pressure is increased by pouring a little more

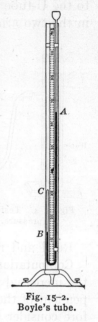

Fig. 15-2.
Boyle's tube.

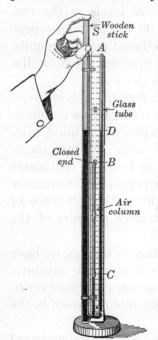

Fig. 15-3. Changing the pressure by means of a plunger.

mercury into the open tube and reading the positions of B and A. Great care must be taken not to spill the mercury!

Another form of apparatus is the **plunger type** (Fig. 15-3), which does not require any pouring of mercury after it is once set up. It takes much less mercury than is required in the first form of apparatus. In this type there are three upright arms mounted on a base with a meter stick. The large arm is the reservoir for mercury. Its level can be changed by means of a wooden plunger. The other two arms form the usual closed and open tubes of a Boyle's Law apparatus. In use, the mercury levels in the closed and open tubes are read with the plunger held at varying depths in the mercury in the reservoir.

* * * *

Pressure gauges. I. *Gas pressure.* Add enough water to the U-tube to fill it about halfway up. The water levels in the two arms will be at the same height because the air

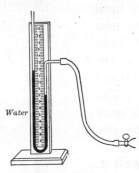

is pressing down equally on both water surfaces. Connect the arm having the elbow by rubber tubing with the gas cock (Fig. 15–4), and turn on the gas slowly. Read and record the position of the water surface in each arm. Compute the difference in water levels in the two arms. Turn off the gas and repeat this operation three times. Compute the mean, or average, value for the difference in water levels.

Water

Fig. 15–4. Testing gas pressure.

Read and record the atmospheric pressure (barometer).

Computations. This difference in water levels is due to the increased pressure caused by the gas. It is quite independent of the cross section of the U-tube. We may therefore consider that this cross section is 1 square centimeter and calculate the pressure in grams per square centimeter of a column of water equal in height to the difference of levels. This may be called the **effective pressure** of the gas.

To get the total, or **absolute, pressure** of the gas, we have to add the effective pressure to the atmospheric pressure. We reduce the barometric reading to grams per square centimeter and add this to the effective pressure expressed in the same unit.

Commercially, gas pressure in this country is expressed in inches of water. Express the effective pressure of the gas tested as inches of water. (1 inch = 2.54 cm.)

Calculate also the total pressure in pounds per square inch, remembering that a pressure of 14.7 pounds per square inch is equivalent to the pressure of a column of mercury 30 inches, or 76 centimeters, in length.

Show clearly each step in your computations.

II. *Lung-pressure.* Set up the mercury manometer as shown in figure 15–5. Record the level of the mercury in the long arm. Then blow *steadily* * for two or three seconds into the mouthpiece, which is connected by rubber tubing with the short arm. While still blowing, pinch the rubber tube hard and then read and record the level of the mercury in the long arm. Each time read the top of the curved mercury-surface.

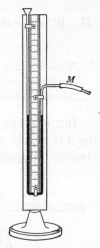

Of course the mercury went down in the short arm as far as it went up in the long arm of the U-tube, and so the difference in mercury levels is *twice* the difference between the two observed readings. Repeat this experiment two or three times and record each trial and the average value of your effective lung-pressure in centimeters of mercury.

Fig. 15–5. Manometer for lung-pressure.

Calculations. Express this effective lung-pressure as grams per square centimeter, also as pounds per square inch, and in atmospheres.

* If you give a quick hard blow into the mouthpiece of the mercury manometer, you will get a higher reading of the mercury than your true lung-pressure. *Why?*

EXPERIMENT 16

BREAKING STRENGTH OF WIRE

I. *How much force is needed to break wires of various materials?*

II. *What is the tensile strength (kilograms per square millimeter) for each material?*

Wire-breaking apparatus   Spools of steel piano wire, brass wire,
Spring balance (10 kg.)   and copper wire, both soft and hard
Micrometer caliper   drawn (about No. 28 A.W.G.)

Introduction. When a rope is used to tow an automobile or a boat, the rope is said to be in a state of **tension.** If the tensile strength is not enough for the purpose, the rope

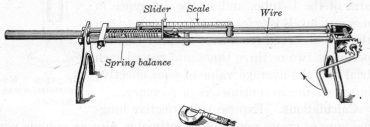

Fig. 16–1. Testing the breaking strength of wire.

breaks. Thus it will readily be seen that one of the most important physical properties of materials is their tensile strength. It may be expressed in pounds per square inch or as kilograms per square millimeter. In our experiment we shall find the breaking strength of wires of various materials and then compute the strength in kilograms per square millimeter on the assumption that the tensile strength varies directly as the area of cross section.

Directions. The apparatus shown in figure 16–1 is so designed that the tension on the wire at the instant it breaks is recorded on a spring balance. The tension is applied by means of a crank. This turns an axle on which the wire is wound. The other end of the wire is attached to the spring balance by means of a frame. When this frame is pulled, a small metal indicator slides along the graduated scale as the spring stretches. The indicator is left just where it was at the instant of breaking.*

First slip one end of the wire through the hole in the crankshaft and bend the end over sharply so that it extends along the shaft. In this way one or two turns of the handle will cause the wire to wind over the end and so fasten it securely. Pass the other end of the wire a couple of times around the post on the sliding frame and clamp the end under the binding post. There must be no kinks or short bends in the wire. Set the pawl so that it will rest on the toothed wheel attached to the shaft and prevent the shaft from turning backward.

Now turn the crank slowly and cause a slight tension in the wire. Measure with a micrometer caliper† the diameter of

---

* If this testing machine is not available, the wire can be fastened at one end to some firm support, such as a gas pipe, and at the other end to the hook of a spring balance. The stress is furnished by pulling with the hands on the spring balance. Another method is to suspend a pail by the wire to be tested. One end of the wire is attached to some stout iron rod clamped so as to project over the edge of the table. Now weights are gradually added until the wire breaks. Then the pail and contents are weighed with a spring balance.

† **Micrometer caliper.** This instrument (Fig. 16–2) is used to measure the diameter of wires, rods, and spheres, and the thickness of sheet metal. It consists of a screw moving in a nut toward or away from a fixed stop. The distance between

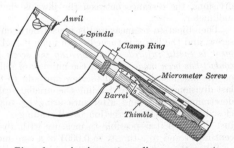

Fig. 16–2. A micrometer caliper measures to 0.001 of a millimeter.

the threads of the screw (if metric) is usually 0.5 of a millimeter. Therefore one complete revolution of the milled head changes the distance between the jaws by exactly 0.5 of a millimeter — a fraction of a turn by a proportional the wire to one hundredth of a millimeter, and increase the tension on the wire by turning the crank until the wire breaks. The reading at the left of the indicator is its breaking strength. Record this force in kilograms.

Repeat the experiment, using a new piece of wire, and find the average of these readings for the breaking strength of the given specimen of spring brass wire. Reject any trials in which the wire breaks at either fastening. If time permits, test also steel wire and copper wire.

Computations. Compute the cross-sectional area ($\frac{1}{4}\pi D^2$, or $0.785\ D^2$) of each kind of wire, using the mean value of the diameters as measured. Then calculate the tensile strength (kilograms per square millimeter) of each material from the fact that the breaking strength varies directly as the area of cross section. That is,

$$\text{Tensile strength (kg./mm.}^2) = \frac{\text{breaking force (kg.)}}{\text{cross section (mm.}^2)}$$

Compare your values of the tensile strength with those given in Table V (Appendix). Why are the results of this experiment only approximate?

amount. The head of the screw (which is inside the sleeve) is divided into 50 divisions. Therefore, when the head is turned through one of these small divisions, the distance between the jaws is changed $\frac{1}{50}$ of 0.5, or 0.01 of a millimeter.

The object to be measured is placed between the stop and the end of the screw, and the latter is turned down upon it. *Avoid undue force as the instrument is easily injured. Stop turning the screw just as soon as you feel that contact has been made.* Count the number of millimeters and half millimeters on the linear scale exposed to view and add to this result the fraction of the last division obtained by reading the circular scale. The zero error should be determined before and after measuring by taking readings with the jaws closed. Apply this correction to all readings. With the micrometer caliper just described it is possible to measure with absolute certainty to 0.001 of a centimeter and to estimate to 0.0001 of a centimeter.

When the micrometer screw is graduated in the English system, the pitch of the screw is generally $\frac{1}{40}$, or 0.025 of an inch. The linear scale is divided into tenths of an inch and each tenth into four equal parts, or fortieths (0.025) of an inch. The head of the screw is divided into twenty-five equal parts. Therefore, when the screw is turned through one division on the circular scale, the screw moves lengthwise $\frac{1}{25}$ of 0.025, or 0.001 of an inch.

The data and results may well be recorded in tabular form as follows:

KIND OF WIRE	DIAMETERS	CROSS SECTION	BREAKING FORCE	TENSILE STRENGTH
Spring brass	— mm.	— mm.²	— kg.	
Mean	—	—	—	kg./mm.²

EXPERIMENT 17

ELASTICITY OF SPIRAL SPRINGS — HOOKE'S LAW

How does the stretching of a spring vary with the force applied, provided the elastic limit is not exceeded?

Spiral (door) spring   Meter rod and support
Set of weights   Marker
              Hanger or pan for weights

Introduction. We have already seen in Experiment 16 that when a force which is more than the tensile strength of a wire is applied to it, the wire snaps or breaks. But if we apply the load gradually, each time removing the load, we shall find that the wire stretches and, up to a certain load (called the **elastic limit**), recovers its initial length again. This property of a material is called its **elasticity.**

We make use of this property of spiral springs in spring balances, door-closing devices, and the shock absorbers used on automobiles. In this experiment we shall determine how the stretching or elongation of a spiral spring varies with the force applied. This relation is known as Hooke's Law because it was first stated about 1678 by an Englishman named Robert Hooke.

Directions. Suspend the spring from some convenient support and attach at the lower end a hanger or pan for the weights. Fasten the marker also to the lower end of the spring. Set up the meter stick vertically very near the marker but not quite touching it (Fig. 17–1). Note the position of the marker on the scale,* reading to tenths of millimeters, and record this as the zero reading.

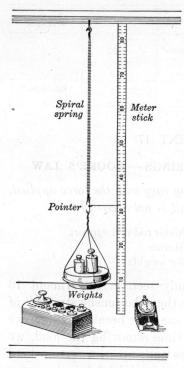

Place a 100-gram weight on the hanger or pan; note the position of the marker and record as before.

Remove the load and record the no-load reading. Now place a 200-gram weight on the hanger, read, and record as before.

In this way gradually increase the load up to 500 grams and after each loading remove the weights and record the zero reading. Each time the marker should very nearly, if not quite, return to its initial reading. If it does not so return approximately, the spring has stretched beyond its elastic limit.

Fig. 17–1. Testing the elasticity of a door spring.

Tabulate the data and results as follows:

LOAD	ZERO READING OF MARKER	READING OF MARKER WITH LOAD	STRETCH OF SPRING
100 g. 200 g. 300 g. 400 g. 500 g.	— —.— — cm.	— —.— — cm.	—.— — cm.

* Avoid the error called *parallax* by keeping the eye in such a position that the line of sight is perpendicular to the scale.

Results. *State the numerical relation which you have found to exist* (except for small experimental errors) *between the stretching of the spiral spring and the corresponding forces applied to it.*

If time permits, plot a curve on cross-section paper to show graphically the relation between the stretch of the spring and the force applied. Let the distances along the X-axis (horizontally) represent the forces and the distances along the Y-axis (vertically) represent the stretches. Choose a scale for plotting the quantities so that the graph will occupy nearly a full page of co-ordinate paper.

*   *   *   *

Vibrations of a spring. It can easily be demonstrated that when a spiral spring is hung from a fixed support with a weight attached at its lower end, the weight will rise and fall with simple vibratory motion. From fundamental laws it can be proved* that the period of oscillation is given by the equation:

$$T = 2\pi\sqrt{\frac{m}{k}}$$

where T = the time in *seconds* of one complete vibration

   m = mass in *grams*

   k = the stiffness factor of the spring; *i.e.*, the force in *dynes* required to stretch the spring *1 cm.*
   (980 dynes = 1 gram)

With a given weight (mass) attached at the lower end of the spring, we can with a stop watch measure the time required for a given number of complete oscillations. From the results of the first part of the experiment, we can compute the stiffness factor. In this way we may check experimentally the mathematical equation given above.

* BLACK'S *Introductory Course in College Physics*, The Macmillan Co., page 207.

MECHANICS (*continued*)

BLOCK III. FORCES AND MOTIONS

Suggestive Questions

1. *If two men pull on a rope, one at each end and each with a force of 20 pounds, what is the tension in the rope?*

2. *Why is there always a sag in telephone lines?*

3. *If a man pushes a lawn-roller with a force of 50 pounds along the handle, which makes an angle of 45° with the horizontal, how much force is used in moving the roller forward?*

4. *Would a pendulum clock run faster or slower on Pikes Peak than in Boston?*

5. *Why does an automobile engine require more gasoline in accelerating than when running at constant speed?*

6. *Does a big rock fall from a cliff more rapidly than a small stone?*

7. *When you sit in a chair, does the chair do any work?*

8. *What effect does the weight of the pendulum bob have upon its period of oscillation?*

9. *What keeps the pendulum swinging in a clock?*

10. *When a rock falls to the ground, is all its energy given up?*

11. *In what way is energy supplied to a bicycle?*

12. *Why have most people given up trying to build "perpetual-motion" machines?*

13. *Where does the energy come from in a windmill?*

14. *Why is it easier for an automobile to climb a hill if it has a running start than if it starts from rest?*

15. *When an apple falls from a tree, what is its potential energy as it rests on the ground?*

EXPERIMENT 18

CONCURRENT FORCES — PARALLELOGRAM LAW

When three nonparallel forces are acting on a body, what must be their relative directions and magnitudes in order to produce equilibrium?

Three spring balances (2000 g.)	Cord (fish line)
Three table clamps	Block of wood
30-cm. rule	Pencil compass

Introduction. Thus far we have been studying machines in which the forces are parallel. In many practical structures, however, such as roofs and bridges, and in many machines, such as sailboats and airplanes, we have several forces which are applied at the same point or, if extended, pass through the same point. Such forces are called **concurrent forces.** In this experiment we shall study the conditions under which concurrent forces are in equilibrium, that is, balance each other so that no motion is produced.

It will greatly simplify the solution of such problems if we represent each force by an arrow drawn to scale. The length of the arrow will show the magnitude of the force, its tip will show the direction of the force, and the tail of the arrow will show the point of application of the force.

Directions. To the middle of a piece of fish line about 40 cm. long, tie a second piece about half as long. At each of the free ends make a loop and attach the hook of a spring balance. To the ring of each balance attach a strong string, and then arrange on the table the clamps, balances, and strings as shown in figure 18–1.*

* In some laboratories it may be more convenient to arrange the apparatus in a vertical plane, using a weight and two spring balances (Fig. 18–2), or three weights and two fixed pulleys. To prevent slipping of the cords at the knot, a small ring (about 1 cm. in diameter) is sometimes used.

Pull each balance until its index is about in the middle of the scale, where it is most reliable, and then slip a right-hand page of the notebook under the line connecting the balances so that the knot comes in about the middle of the page.

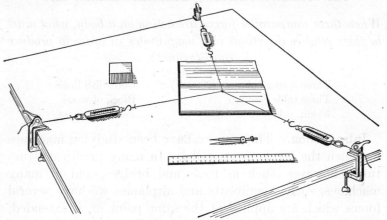

Fig. 18-1.   Three concurrent forces in equilibrium.

In order to show the direction of each cord on the paper, place a rectangular block alongside and draw a line directly under each cord.   Record beside each line the force indicated by the balance, and then relieve the tension on the spring balances.   Observe the zero reading of each balance in a horizontal position and apply the proper correction to the reading just recorded.   If the zero reading is less than zero, add the correction to the balance reading recorded on the paper ; if it is more than zero, subtract the proper amount.

Graphical construction.   If the experiment has been carefully done, the three lines representing the three forces will, when prolonged, intersect at a common point.   Measure off on each line a distance corresponding to the force, according to any convenient scale, such as 200 grams to 1 centimeter. Make an arrowhead at the end of each measured line and erase that part of the line which lies beyond the arrowhead.

On any two of these lines construct a parallelogram, using

a ruler and pencil compass to get the lines exactly parallel. Draw the three original force lines (*OA*, *OB*, and *OW*) as solid lines, the lines needed to complete the parallelogram (*BR* and *AR*) as dotted lines, and the diagonal (*OR*) as a broken line (Fig. 18–2). Measure the diagonal of this parallelogram *OARB* from the central point *O*, and compute the magnitude of the force which it represents. For example, when the scale is 200 grams to 1 centimeter, a line 15.6 centimeters

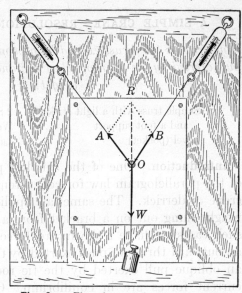

Fig. 18–2. Three forces acting at one point *O*.

long represents a force of 3120 grams. This diagonal line represents the **resultant** of the two forces *OA* and *OB* which form the sides of the parallelogram.

The third force *OW*, which balances these two forces *OA* and *OB*, is called their **equilibrant.**

How does the resultant of two forces compare with their equilibrant (a) in magnitude and (b) in direction?

In a similar way determine the resultant of each of the other pairs of forces, regarding the third force in each case as the equilibrant.

If time permits, make a second trial, using different angles and forces, and repeat the constructions on another page.

State in your notebook what you have proved to be true regarding both the magnitude and the direction of the resultant of two concurrent forces.

EXPERIMENT 19

A SIMPLE CRANE. RESOLUTION OF A FORCE

How great is the thrust exerted by a boom and how great is the pull exerted by the tie rope when a crane is used to support a weight?

Simple truss with a light stick and a foot support	2 Spring balances
	Weights and hanger
Level (pocket)	Large protractor

Introduction. One of the simplest practical applications of the parallelogram law for concurrent forces is found in a crane or derrick. The same law applies to the case of any weight hung out on a bracket from a pole or wall. In all such cases we have a downward force caused by the load, an outward thrust or push exerted by the boom or stick, and an oblique pull exerted by the tie rod. These three concurrent forces are in equilibrium. Our problem in this experiment is to find how much is the thrust exerted by the boom and how much is the pull exerted by the tie rod when we know the load and the direction of the other two forces. In this experiment we shall be able to check the accuracy of our computed values for these forces by actually measuring each force with a spring balance. From our experience in the solution of such problems, we may develop a certain amount of practical sense which will enable us to solve such problems approximately, even without experimenting.

Directions. *Boom horizontal.* Figure 19–1 shows a laboratory model of a simple crane, or truss, in which the weight of the stick *BF* may be neglected because it is so small in comparison with the other forces. Set up the apparatus so that the stick is horizontal. Test this by placing the level on the stick *BF*. Add enough weights at *W* to stretch the balance *T* nearly to its full scale reading.

Record the load W and the pull exerted by the tie rope as indicated by the balance T.   To measure the thrust exerted by the stick, attach a second balance P at the outer end of the stick and pull out in line with the stick until the end of the stick at F just leaves the support.

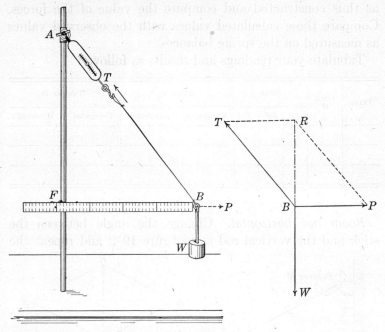

Fig. 19–1.   Model of crane with boom horizontal and arrow-diagram.

To get the angles of the triangle, it will be convenient to measure the dimensions (cm.) of the three sides AF, BF, and AB.   These sides can then be drawn to scale in the notebook and the angles measured with a protractor.

To compute the force exerted by the tie rope, we have merely to draw carefully an *arrow-diagram* of the three forces acting at the point B.   Use a full page for this diagram and make the scale as large as the space will permit.   First lay off to scale the vertical line BW to represent the weight,

then draw the force lines to show the direction of the thrust
and of the pull. Extend upward the weight line *BW* as a
dashed line its own length *BR*, and from *R* construct parallel
dotted lines *RT* and *RP*. Where these lines cut the force
lines, place arrowheads. Measure these forces *BT* and *BP*
as thus constructed and compute the value of the forces.
Compare these calculated values with the observed values
as measured on the spring balances.

Tabulate your readings and results as follows:

TRIAL	LOAD W	SIDES			PULL T		THRUST P	
		AF	BF	AB	Computed	Measured	Computed	Measured

*   *   *   *

Boom not horizontal. Change the angle between the
stick and the vertical rod as in figure 19-2 and repeat the

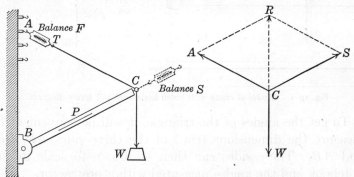

Fig. 19-2. Forces acting on the end of boom at *C*.

experiment, making the arrow-diagram and taking the check
readings as before.

If time permits, set the boom at some other angle and get
a third set of readings.

Tabulate your readings and results as follows:

Trial	Load W	Sides			Pull T		Thrust S	
		AC	BC	AB	Computed	Measured	Computed	Measured

EXPERIMENT 20

ACCELERATED MOTION

How does the distance traversed by a body moving with constant acceleration vary with the time?

Grooved plank (Duff's)
Steel ball (1.5″ diam.)
Support for one end of incline

Meter stick
Pepper box with lycopodium powder
Cloth and damp sponge

Introduction. A certain automobile was advertised as being able to start from rest and in 20 seconds to acquire a speed of 60 miles an hour. Assuming that it "picked up" speed at a uniform rate, this would mean that it gained speed at the rate of 3 miles an hour each second. In other words, its **acceleration** is 3 miles-per-hour per second, or 4.4 feet-per-second per second. It is quite likely that the automobile did not gain speed at a uniform rate, but actual problems involving nonuniform acceleration are too difficult for us to solve at present.

The first careful study of accelerated motion was made by Galileo early in the seventeenth century. He rolled a ball down a long inclined groove, but had great difficulty in measuring short intervals of time. We can now repeat Galileo's experiment with apparatus improved so as to record short equal intervals of time. In this experiment we shall try to find the relation between the *distance* traversed by a ball moving at a uniformly accelerated speed and the *time* which has elapsed during its motion.

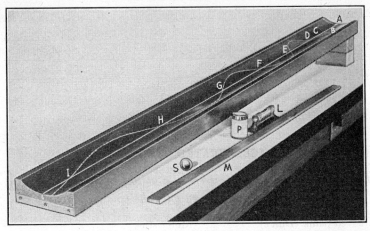

Fig. 20–1.   Accelerated motion of a steel ball *S* down an inclined groove.

We shall use a plank about 4 feet long with a broad groove in the center.   When the grooved plank (Fig. 20–1) is placed horizontally on the table, a steel ball placed on one edge will, when released, oscillate back and forth like a pendulum. Although the swings decrease in amplitude, yet the time of each swing remains constant.   When the plank is tilted so that one end is higher than the other, a ball placed at the top in the middle of the groove will roll down, going faster and faster until it reaches the bottom.

In this experiment we shall combine the oscillatory motion back and forth across the groove with this accelerated motion down the incline in such a way as to make the oscillatory motion mark off equal intervals of time for the study of the accelerated motion.

Directions.   First wipe off the trough with a damp sponge and rub it thoroughly dry with a cloth.   Then sprinkle it with lycopodium powder.   Raise one end of the plank 10 or

20 cm. above the table, taking care to keep the under edges at the upper and lower ends exactly horizontal. Place the ball at the top of the groove against the metal strip which serves as a guide until it reaches the middle line. When the ball is released, it goes zigzagging down the groove. If the powder is now blown off, we see distinctly the path traced on the black board, somewhat as shown in figure 20-2. We have now simply to measure certain distances along the mid-line to understand the relation of *distance* to *time* in a case of accelerated motion.

Fig. 20-2. The curve traced.

Record the data and results in tabular form as below.

In the second column we record the distances traversed in 1 interval of time, 2 intervals, 3, and so on; that is, AB, AC, AD, AE, etc.

In the third column we record the separate distances covered in the first interval of time, in the second interval, and so on; that is, AB, BC, CD, etc.

TIME INTER-VALS (t)	SPACE TRAV-ERSED (s)	DISTANCE COVERED IN EACH TIME INTERVAL (d)	$\frac{s}{t^2}$	$\frac{d}{2\,t-1}$
1				
2				
3				
4				
5				

Results. From a study of the results given in the fourth column $\left(\frac{s}{t^2}\right)$, *what relation seems to exist between the space s and the time t?* From a study of the results in the last column

$\left(\dfrac{d}{2\,t-1}\right)$, *what relation seems to exist between the separate distances d and the odd numbers given by the expression* $(2\,t-1)$?

*   *   *   *

Study of projectiles. In studying projectiles we have the resultant of two motions, one essentially uniform due to the gun and the other accelerated due to gravity. We may conveniently study this problem with Packard's Inclined Plane (Fig. 20–3).* In this experiment a steel ball is given

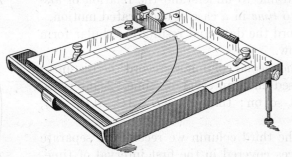

Fig. 20–3.   Packard's apparatus for studying projectiles.

a uniform velocity horizontally and at the same time has an accelerated motion downward. The ball in rolling down the inclined plane over a thin sheet of carbon paper traces a curve on the underlying cross-section paper. By studying this curve we may arrive at the laws of accelerated motion. Further directions accompany the apparatus.

* This was designed by Mr. J. C. Packard of the Brookline (Mass.) High School.

EXPERIMENT 21

THE SIMPLE PENDULUM

*What is the value of **g** (the acceleration of gravity) as measured by a simple pendulum?*

Ball, lead or iron (about 0.75 inch in diam.)	Stop watch or clock with second hand
Linen thread (waxed) or wire (No. 28) about 2 m. long	Vernier caliper
Support with clamp	Meter stick

Introduction. Everyone is familiar with the pendulum as used in clocks, where it acts as a regulator. It is possible to measure the acceleration of gravity by getting the time of a body falling freely through a known distance. But this method does not give as precise results as can be obtained in experiments with a pendulum. It can be proved * mathematically that the fundamental equation for a simple pendulum is

$$T = 2 \pi \sqrt{\frac{l}{g}}$$

where T is the time in seconds of a complete (back and forth) vibration, l is the length of the pendulum in centimeters, g is the acceleration of gravity in centimeters-per-second per second, and π is 3.14. We can measure T and l directly and π is known, so we may compute the value of g. For this purpose it will be well to use the equation in this form:

$$g = \frac{4 \pi^2 l}{T^2}.$$

To measure the time T of one vibration, that is, from one end of its arc to the other and back again, we shall get the time for 50 vibrations and then compute the *period* of the pendulum, or the time that one vibration takes. To deter-

---

* BLACK'S *Introductory Course in College Physics*, p. 206.

mine the length l of a pendulum (where the weight of the supporting thread or wire is negligible), we measure the distance from the lower edge of the support to the center of the ball, or "bob."

Directions. Attach the bob to a thread about 180 centimeters long and suspend it from the supporting clamp (Fig. 21–1). A bit of sealing wax will hold the thread to the metal ball. When the pendulum comes to rest, fasten a sheet of paper directly back of the bob so that a vertical black line, which has been ruled on the paper, will indicate the position of rest of the pendulum.

Fig. 21–1. Two pendulums.

Set the pendulum to swinging through a short arc. As soon as its motion becomes uniform, start the stop watch just as the bob passes its position of rest, and at the same time begin counting *zero, one, two, three,* etc., every time the bob passes its position of rest in one direction. Stop the watch as the bob passes its position of rest on the *fiftieth* swing.* Make a second determination of the length of time required for 50 vibrations as before. If the work has been done carefully, these two determinations should agree very closely, probably within one second. From the mean value for the time compute the period, or time, of one swing T.

Measure the distance from the supporting clamp to the upper surface of the ball (to 0.1 cm.) and add to this half the diameter as measured with the caliper to the same degree of accuracy. This is to be considered the approximate length l of the pendulum. Having thus measured T and l directly and knowing the value of π, compute the value of g.

---

* If a stop watch is not available, this experiment can be performed with a clock or watch which is provided with a second hand. It will be well to have two students work together, one to watch and count the pendulum swings and the other to watch the clock and record the hour, minute, and second of the start and finish.

If time permits, repeat the experiment, using a shorter pendulum.

Tabulate your data and results as follows:

Length of Pendulum (l)	Time of 50 Vibrations			Period (T)	Value of g
	Trial 1	Trial 2	Mean		
				Mean =	

* * * *

More about pendulums. Find whether the time of vibration is affected by varying the *size* or *material* of the bob used, provided the length of the pendulum is not changed.

Also find what effect, if any, a variation of *amplitude* of vibration has upon the time of vibration.

If an open staircase is available, it will be interesting to set up a very long pendulum (50 ft. or more). It will be well to use an iron ball supported by a steel wire. In this case it is easily possible to time one hundred swings and so get the period with considerable precision. The length of the wire should be measured with a measuring tape.

EXPERIMENT 22

TIME OF A FALLING BODY

I. *How long does it take a freely falling ball to drop a measured distance?*

II. *What is the acceleration, due to gravity, in centimeters-per-second per second?*

2-meter pendulum bar	Stop watch
Steel ball	Measuring stick

Introduction. In this experiment we shall allow a steel ball to drop 2 or 3 meters and shall measure the time of this

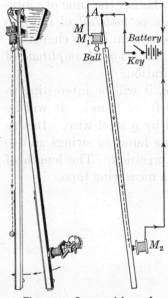

Fig. 22–1. Improved form of Whiting's pendulum.

fall by means of an improved form of the Whiting pendulum (Fig. 22–1). Since the time for such a fall is very short, it requires considerable skill to measure the time interval with some precision and certainty. The pendulum consists of a rod made of wood or, better, square brass tube 2 to 3 meters long and about 4 centimeters square. This is hung by means of a thin strip of leather or steel so that the ball in falling will just graze the side of the pendulum along its entire length. If the pendulum is pulled to one side and then released at the same instant at which the ball is released, the ball will strike the pendulum as it swings through its midpoint. We can find the point where the ball struck the pendulum by attaching a strip of white paper covered with a carbon-paper strip to the side of the pendulum rod near the point where the ball hits. The distance which the ball falls can be determined by measuring the distance between the initial position of the ball and the spot where it hit the pendulum. The time for the ball to drop this distance is one quarter that of a complete vibration (double swing) of the pendulum.

In the fundamental equation for falling bodies, $s = \frac{1}{2} gt^2$, we know s, the distance, and t, the time; so we can easily compute the value of g, the acceleration. Since the time t enters into this equation as the square, it is essential that we measure this factor as accurately as possible.

Directions. Set the pendulum vibrating and carefully determine the time for 50 complete vibrations by the use of a stop watch. A complete vibration means a swing to and fro. Try to estimate the time to the fraction (0.2) of a second so as to obtain the value as precisely as possible. This is the greatest source of error in this experiment. Make at least *three* trials of 50 each. Attach a strip of white paper to the outer face of the pendulum. Place a strip of carbon paper over the white paper. A ball is suspended by means of an electromagnet so that it hangs just at the upper end of the pendulum. This ball is so adjusted that it will just touch the pendulum anywhere along its length when the bar is hanging vertically. When the ball has been placed in the position shown in the diagram, measure very carefully the distance from the center of the ball to the floor.

The pendulum is also held back by an electromagnet and is so connected that it is released by the same switch as releases the ball. Thus the pendulum and ball are released at the same instant. Just as the pendulum completes a quarter of a complete vibration, it strikes the ball so that a black mark is printed on the paper. Measure carefully the distance from the center of this mark to the floor and compute how far the ball fell before it struck the pendulum.

The time (t) required for the ball to fall this distance (s) is found by taking one-quarter of the period found in the first part of the experiment. Make *ten* trials. A box of sand may well be placed below the pendulum to catch the falling ball.

Computations. Find the average time and the average distance and compute the acceleration due to gravity in centimeters-per-second per second, using the formula for the distance covered by a ball falling from rest ($s = \frac{1}{2} gt^2$).

Compute the percentage error, assuming $g = 980$ cm./sec.^{2}

Compute the probable error. In the *time* values, take the difference between the average value and the value most remote from it. Find what per cent this is of the average value. Do the same for the *distance* readings.

Since the time occurs twice (t^2), multiply the probable percentage error in time by 2.

Add the two percentage errors. This gives an approximate value of the **probable error.**

EXPERIMENT 23

CENTRIPETAL FORCE

How much force is required to keep a body of known mass revolving in a circular path of known radius at constant angular velocity?

Centripetal force app. (Cenco)	Weight hanger
Friction-drive rotator, motor driven	Slotted weights, 2 kg. to 10 g.
	Support stand
Vernier caliper	Stop watch

Introduction. When a given mass is revolving in a circular path, it has a tendency to continue in a straight line tangent to the circle. The constraining force which keeps it in the circular path and acts always at right angles to the circular path is called the **centripetal force.** It is possible to compute the amount of this force from Newton's Second Law, $F = \dfrac{W}{g} a$.

In the case of circular motion, the acceleration toward the center can be shown * to be equal to the linear velocity squared divided by the radius; that is, $a = v^2/r$. Therefore the centripetal force $F = \dfrac{W v^2}{gr}$. In this experiment a spring provides the centripetal force. One end of the spring is fastened to the frame, which can be whirled at different speeds by means of a rotator (Fig. 23–1). The other end of the spring is attached to a cylindrical mass M of known weight.

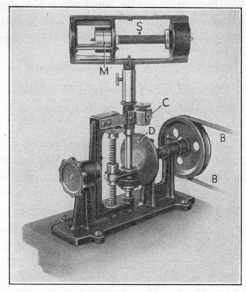

Fig. 23–1. A variable speed rotator used to whirl the mass M about a vertical axis.

When the frame is rotated at increasing speed, the mass moves outward and at a definite speed of rotation occupies a definite position, as shown by the little indicating lever. The radius of the circle described by the center of mass when the indicator shows "balance" is represented by r in the equation. The linear speed v is measured by getting the number of revolutions per minute (r.p.m.) by means of a revolution counter and watch.

$$v = 2 \pi r \times \frac{\text{r.p.m.}}{60}.$$

* BLACK's *Introductory Course in College Physics*, The Macmillan Company, page 184.

The rotating frame is now removed from the rotator and suspended so that the axis of the spring and cylindrical mass is vertical.   Weights are then applied to stretch the spring until the mass is in the position of "balance," as shown by the indicator.   The total force F necessary to produce the same stretch of the spring is thus found, and this force is compared with the computed force obtained by substituting the proper values in the equation $F = \dfrac{Wv^2}{gr}$.

Directions.   The weight W of the cylindrical mass will be found stamped on the cylinder.   The value of g may be assumed to be 980 cm./sec.[2].   The radius r may be conveniently measured by the vernier caliper when the spring is stretched by the weights in vertical position to a condition of "balance."   The determination of the speed of rotation

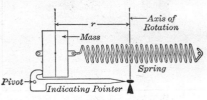

Fig. 23–2.   Pointer and its index.

which is just enough to produce the desired tension requires several trials and some practice observations.   By means of an adjusting screw on the rotator, it is possible to manipulate the speed until the pointer indicates "balance."   This is shown when the pointer-tip vibrates up and down through a range of about 5 mm. and the middle of this range is opposite the sharp edge of a fixed index (Fig. 23–2).   To determine the speed (r.p.m.), hold the revolution counter against the gear on the spindle for exactly one minute.   Record the initial reading of the revolution counter and also the reading after a one-minute interval.   Repeat this for at least *five* independent observations of speed.   During these tests it is well to keep the attention fixed on the tip of the indicator and to adjust the speed so as to maintain the condition of "balance."

To measure the relatively large force exerted on the spring, suspend the frame vertically and attach sufficient weights to stretch the spring so that the tip of the indicator stands opposite the index (Fig. 23-3). The oscillation of the weights up and down may sometimes cause the pointer to tip over beyond the position of equilibrium. But the pointer may be brought back to its correct position by touching it lightly with a pencil. The total force F applied to the spring includes the weight of the cylinder as well as the weight of the hanger and its added weights. When the final adjustment of the weight has been made and recorded, the distance between the mid-line of the cylindrical mass and the mid-line of the rotating frame should be measured several times and the average value recorded as the radius r.

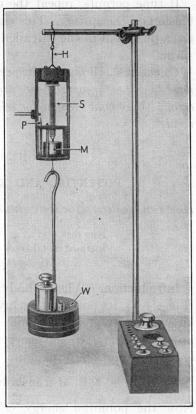

Fig. 23-3. Testing the spring S.

Computations. Compute the linear velocity v (cm./sec.) from the revolutions per second (r.p.s.) and the circumference ($2\pi r$). To calculate the centripetal force F in grams, we have merely to substitute in the formula $\dfrac{Wv^2}{gr}$, where W is the weight of the rotating mass in grams, v is the linear velocity in cm./sec., g is 980 cm./sec.², and r is the radius in centimeters. Compare this value obtained by computation with the experimental value F.

If time permits, repeat the experiment, using a different tension on the spring. This can easily be done by changing the adjustment of the threaded collar at the fixed end of the spring.

Questions. *What is the percentage error in your experiment? What measurement probably introduces the largest error? Give your reasons for selecting this particular measurement.*

EXPERIMENT 24

POTENTIAL AND KINETIC ENERGY

How can we determine the rotational energy of a disk and axle?

Iron disk and axle	Meter stick
Inclined metal track	Stop watch
Micrometer caliper	

Introduction. When a body rolls down an inclined track (Fig. 24–1), its potential energy at the top is converted into kinetic energy at the bottom. This kinetic energy is made up of two parts, (*a*) the energy of linear motion and (*b*) the energy of rotation, or of spin. That is,

P.E. = K.E. of translation + K.E. of rotation.

Now the potential energy ($P.E.$) in gram-centimeters is easily computed from the weight (W) in grams and the height (h) in centimeters of the track at the top above that at the bottom.

$$\textbf{P.E.} = W \times h$$

The kinetic energy of translation, or of linear motion, is computed by the usual formula (§ **165**).

$$\textbf{K.E.} = \frac{Wv^2}{2\,g}.$$

To get the velocity v of the disk at the bottom of the track, we first compute its *average velocity*. Then, since it starts at rest, the final velocity v is just twice the average velocity. To get this average velocity (cm./sec.), we measure the

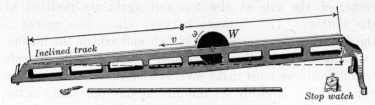

Fig. 24–1. Rolling a disk and axle down an inclined track.

distance s (cm.) along the inclined track and the time t (sec.) which the disk takes to roll down. Note that this is an excellent case of uniformly accelerated motion. Therefore,

$$v = \frac{2\,s}{t}.$$

We may assume that g is 980 cm./sec.[2] the kinetic energy of translation and then calculate $\frac{Wv^2}{2\,g}$.

Finally, to determine the energy of spin, we have merely to subtract the kinetic energy of translation $\left(\frac{Wv^2}{2\,g}\right)$ from the potential energy (Wh).

Directions. In setting up the inclined tracks, it is important to have the tracks exactly level from side to side and absolutely free from dirt and grease. The weight of the disk and axle in grams has been stamped upon it and should be noted as W. To get the vertical height between its position at the top and bottom, first hold the axle against the two stops at the top of the track and measure the vertical distance from the center of the axle to the table. In the same way, when the disk and axle reaches the bottom, measure the vertical distance from the center of the axle to the table. From these two distances we can compute the vertical height (h)

of the disk at the top of the track above its position at the bottom.

To measure the distance (s) which it rolls down along the inclined track, it will be well to mark the position of the center of the axle at the top and again its position at the bottom. The distance between these two marks is the distance (s) traversed by the disk and axle on the incline.

To measure the time (t) required for the disk and axle to roll down, we must make several trials and use the average value. First carefully set the disk at the top *exactly* in the center of the track. Then measure with a stop watch the time to one fifth of a second required to roll to the bottom. If the disk touches the sides of the track, this trial must be discarded.

Tabulate your data somewhat as follows:

Data

Weight of disk and axle (W) . . . .   g.
Distance of axle at top above table . . . .   cm.
Distance of axle at bottom above table . . . .   cm.
    Vertical height (h) . . . .   cm.
Length of inclined track (s) . . . .   cm.
Time required to roll down . . . .   sec.
    "   "   "   "   " . . . .   sec.
    "   "   "   "   " . . . .   sec.
    Average time (t) . . . .   sec.

Computations

Potential energy loss $(W \times h)$ . . . .   g.-cm.

Final velocity at bottom $\left(v = \dfrac{2\,s}{t}\right)$ . . . .   cm./sec.

Kinetic energy of translation $\left(\dfrac{Wv^2}{2\,g}\right)$ . . . . .   g.-cm.

Kinetic energy of spin . . . .   **g.-cm.**

Results. *State the fundamental law which is assumed in this experiment. Which is the greater, the energy of spin or the energy of translation? Which measurement introduces the greatest uncertainty in the final result? Why?*

* * * *

Rotational inertia. It is quite possible to get more information about rotation from this experiment. For example, we can compute its **angular speed** and its **rotational inertia.** Engineers often express the speed of a rotating body as revolutions per minute (r.p.m.) and sometimes as *radians per second* (ω), where the radian is an angle which has an arc equal to the radius, or about 57.3°.

$$\text{Speed in radians per second } (\omega) = \frac{\text{linear speed } (v)}{\text{radius } (r)}.$$

The radius of the axle on which the disk rolls down the incline is the radius (r).

The **rotational inertia** of a body is its inertia as regards rotation. This property of a body depends not only on its weight (or mass) but also on the way this mass is distributed about the axis. It can be proved mathematically that the rotational inertia (I) of a cylinder is equal to $\frac{WR^2}{2\,g}$. Now what shall we do with it?

The kinetic energy of rotation can be proved to be equal to $\frac{1}{2} I\omega^2$. It will be interesting to measure the diameter of the axle and compute the radius (r) of the axle; also, to measure the diameter of the disk and compute the radius (R) of the disk. With these data we may compute the angular velocity (ω) of the disk at the bottom of the inclined track and also its rotational inertia (I). From these results we may get the kinetic energy of rotation ($\frac{1}{2} I\omega^2$) and compare this calculated value with the experimental value obtained in the first part of this experiment.

HEAT

BLOCK IV. HEAT ENERGY

Suggestive Questions

1. *Which is more accurate, a centigrade or a Fahrenheit thermometer?*

2. *Is the temperature of melting ice always the same?*

3. *Why does the ice-water pitcher "sweat" on the outside?*

4. *If steam is at the same temperature as boiling water, why does steam have more heat in it than boiling water?*

5. *Does a thermometer measure the heat in a substance?*

6. *What makes the radiator on an automobile sometimes "boil" in winter?*

7. *Do storm windows keep out the cold in winter?*

8. *What is the purpose of the engine fan on an automobile?*

9. *Can you have ice colder than 32° F.?*

10. *Will vegetables cook faster if the water boils more rapidly?*

11. *What is the purpose of an electric motor in an oil-burning furnace?*

12. *In what unit is the energy value of foods expressed?*

13. *Why are the cylinders of a steam engine steam-jacketed?*

14. *How many power strokes are there for each revolution in an eight-cylinder gas engine?*

15. *Why must a gas engine have a flywheel?*

16. *Why is it necessary to connect the engine with the driving shaft of an automobile by means of a clutch?*

EXPERIMENT 25

THE FIXED POINTS OF A THERMOMETER

What is the error in the freezing point (0° C.) and in the boiling point (100° C.) of a thermometer?

Steam generator with cylindrical top	Tumbler or cup
Bunsen burner or alcohol lamp	Clean cracked ice or snow
Thermometer (− 10° to 110° C.)	Barometer

Introduction. Every household should possess several thermometers: an indoor thermometer, an outdoor thermometer, and a clinical, or "fever," thermometer. Besides these, some families have several special thermometers, such as a milk thermometer used in pasteurizing milk, a bath thermometer, and the thermometers used on hot-water-heating boilers and on oven doors. In laboratories the so-called chemical thermometer is most commonly used. It consists of a cylindrical glass tube blown or sealed on the end of a fine-bore glass tube, or "stem." The bulb and part of the stem are filled with mercury and the top is sealed after removing the air. A scale is made either on the glass or on a separate strip of metal. For the ordinary Fahrenheit thermometer the melting point of ice is marked 32° and the boiling point of water 212°, and the distance between is divided into 180 equal degrees. On the centigrade scale the ice point is 0° and the boiling point 100°.

The ordinary household thermometer is generally correct within 1 or 2 degrees, although sometimes there is an error of several degrees. It is so important that clinical thermometers be accurate or at least that the error be known that the National Bureau of Standards at Washington, D. C., tests each year thousands of these thermometers and furnishes a certificate showing the correction to be added to the different scale readings.

In this experiment we shall test the accuracy of a centigrade chemical thermometer at the 0° point and at the 100° point. These two points are called the **fixed points** because each of them represents under certain conditions an invariable temperature.

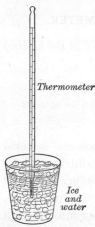

Thermometer

Ice and water

Fig. 25-1. Testing the freezing point.

Directions. Fill the boiler about half full of water, screw the chimney or top down firmly, and start heating the water. In lighting a Bunsen burner, turn on the gas and ignite it by holding the lighted match (or gas lighter) 3 or 4 inches above the burner. Sometimes the flame "strikes back" and burns in the tube. In this case turn off the gas and relight it.

I. *Freezing point.* Fill a glass tumbler with clean, finely chopped ice (or snow) and pour over it enough water to fill the spaces around the pieces of ice. Put the thermometer bulb down into the melting ice (Fig. 25-1) so that the top of the mercury column is just visible when it is near the zero mark. After a few minutes, when the mercury has ceased to fall and has apparently come to a definite position, read the thermometer as closely as possible, estimating to tenths of a degree. Adjust your eye so that your line of vision is as nearly as possible at right angles to the thermometer scale. Record this as the *freezing point* on your thermometer; prefix the plus (+) sign if the reading is above zero or the minus (−) if it is below zero. Thus, + 1.2° or − 0.5° C.

What is the error in the freezing point of your thermometer?

What correction should be added to a reading made on this thermometer near the zero point?

II. *Boiling point.* To test the boiling point, the thermometer is exposed to the steam from boiling water. Carefully insert the thermometer in the stopper of the steam boiler so that the 100° mark on the scale projects just a little above the stopper (Fig. 25–2). Let the steam flow around the bulb and stem for several minutes until the thermometer has come to a fixed reading. Then read and record its position and also the height of the barometer.

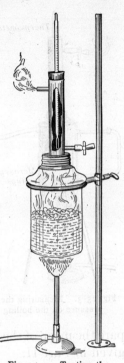

When the barometer stands at 76 centimeters, the boiling point of water is 100° C. At higher pressures the temperature of steam is higher, and at lower pressures it is lower. Careful experiments show that a change of one centimeter in the height of the barometer causes a change of approximately 0.37° C. in the boiling point. For example, if the barometer reads 74.5 centimeters, then the boiling point of water is

$$100 - (1.5 \times 0.37) = 99.4° \text{ C.}$$

Fig. 25–2. Testing the boiling point.

Calculate from the barometric pressure the true boiling point at the time of your experiment.

Compute the error in the boiling point of your thermometer.

What correction should be added to a reading on this thermometer made near the 100° mark?

Record your data and results neatly in tabular form.

* * * *

(a) **Effect of pressure on boiling point.** To determine *how much the pressure of steam must be increased to raise its temperature 1° C.*, attach a pressure gauge to the boiler, as shown in figure 25–3. When the steam is escaping freely into the air at *V*, the mercury * in the gauge reads at the

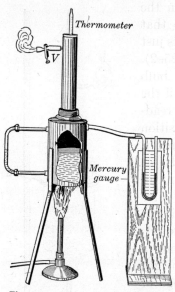

Fig. 25-3. Measuring the effect of pressure on the boiling point.

same level in each arm. If we gradually close the exit *V* by screwing up the pinchcock, the pressure gauge will show a difference in levels. When this difference amounts to 6 or 8 centimeters and has become fairly steady for 2 or 3 minutes, read the thermometer *very carefully.* Then close the pinchcock still further until the difference in level amounts to 8 or 10 centimeters and read again. Make a third trial by loosening the pinchcock a bit. From each of these sets of readings compute the pressure needed to increase the temperature of steam 1° C. Compare the mean of these values with the accepted value already given in Part II.

(*b*) **Testing a household thermometer.** The freezing point (32° F.) is readily tested as described in Part I. Higher points may be tested by placing the thermometer in warm water at about 25° C. and comparing its reading with that of a good laboratory thermometer. Points below the freezing point may be tested by placing both the thermometers in a freezing mixture of ice (or snow), salt, and water.†

* If water is used in the gauge instead of mercury, a taller U-tube must be used or a straight tube dipping into a deep jar of water.

† For further directions about the use and testing of thermometers, consult "Measurements for the Household," *Circular No. 55 of the Bureau of Standards.* U. S. Government Printing Office, Washington, D. C.

LINEAR EXPANSION OF A SOLID

How much does one centimeter of aluminum (or brass) expand when heated one degree centigrade?

Linear expansion apparatus (lever or Cowan form)	Thermometer
	Barometer
Steam generator and burner	Vernier caliper
Meter stick	

Introduction. It is a well-known fact that nearly every solid expands when heated and contracts when cooled. This is made use of in setting steel tires on locomotive wheels and on wagon wheels and has to be allowed for by expansion joints in steel bridges and railway tracks. The exact amount of expansion depends on *three factors:* (1) the material, (2) the length of the object heated, and (3) its change in temperature. This may be expressed as an equation, thus:

$$e = kl(t' - t)$$

where e is the change in length, l the initial length, t' the temperature when hot, and t the temperature when cold. The factor k is the expansion of a unit length for 1 degree rise in temperature and is called the **coefficient of linear expansion.** This factor is a very small decimal fraction and varies with different substances.

In this experiment we shall measure the expansion of a given length of metal when heated from the temperature of the room to that of steam. Then we shall compute the expansion per unit length for one degree centigrade.

Directions. Since the amount which a solid expands when heated is exceedingly small, it is difficult to measure it with great precision. One of the many forms of apparatus used to measure this slight expansion employs a lever to magnify the actual expansion. The metal rod is heated by passing steam through a jacket, as shown in figure 26–1. One end of the rod rests against the stop-screw B, and the other end, as the tube expands, turns a bent lever AFP about the point F. The expansion of the tube is magnified as many times as the short arm AF of the lever is contained in the long arm FP. Therefore, to get the actual expansion, we have merely to divide the rise of the pointer P on the scale S by the magnifying power of the lever.

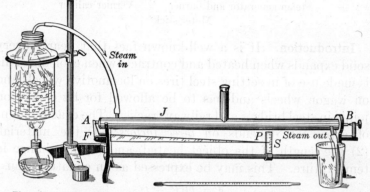

Fig. 26–1.   Measuring the expansion of a rod by means of a bent lever AFP.*

The length of the rod between the fixed point B and the point A, where the bent lever rests against the rod, can easily be measured to three significant figures with an ordinary meter stick without removing it from the jacket. The short arm of the bent lever can be measured with sufficient precision by means of a vernier caliper. If the tube has been in the room for several hours, it may be assumed to be at room temperature. (A more accurate method is to run water of a known temperature through the jacket.) Read very carefully the position of the pointer on the scale, estimating to tenths of a millimeter (0.01 cm.).

Then connect the jacket by rubber tubing with the steam generator and run steam through it until there is no further

---

* An electric heater may well be used instead of a Bunsen burner or alcohol lamp.

movement of the pointer. While the steam is still flowing, read again as carefully as before the position of the pointer and compute the rise of the pointer. All linear measurements should be made in the same units, for example, *all in centimeters.*

The temperature of the steam may best be computed from the barometer reading as explained in Experiment 25.

Compute the actual expansion; also the expansion of a unit length (1 centimeter) per degree centigrade, that is, the coefficient of linear expansion of the metal used.

Record all your data and results in tabular form.

*   *   *   *

Other forms of apparatus. A more accurate and more delicate form of apparatus for this experiment is shown in figure 26–2. In it the expansion is measured by allowing

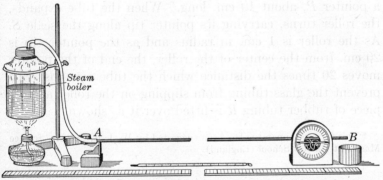

Fig. 26–2. Cowan's apparatus for measuring expansion.

a tube *AB* to rest on a needle, which in turn rests on roller bearings. The rotation of the needle is measured on a circular scale by a pointer. Evidently, if the needle makes one complete revolution, the tube has expanded a distance equal to the circumference of the needle; and if it turns less than a complete revolution, the tube has expanded the corresponding fraction of the circumference of the needle.

The diameter of the needle can be measured with great precision by means of a micrometer caliper.

A third form of apparatus (Fig. 26–3) consists of a glass tube which is about 90 cm. long and 1.0 cm. in diameter. One end is firmly fastened in a rubber stopper B and held in a clamp; the other end of the tube is supported on a brass roller A, of about 2 cm. diameter, to which is attached

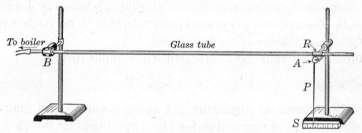

Fig. 26-3.   Calvert's apparatus for measuring expansion.

a pointer P, about 19 cm. long. When the tube expands, the roller turns, carrying its pointer tip along the scale S. As the roller is 1 cm. in radius and as the pointer tip is 20 cm. from the center of the roller, the end of the pointer moves 20 times the distance which the tube expands. To prevent the glass tubing from slipping on the roller a short piece of rubber tubing R is fitted over it as shown.*

* This form of apparatus has been suggested by W. J. R. Calvert, Science Master at Harrow School (England).

CUBICAL EXPANSION OF AIR

What fraction of its volume at 0° C. does a certain quantity of air expand when heated 1° C. under constant pressure?

Charles' Law tube (Waterman)
  mounted on a meter stick
Thermometer

Steam generator with top
Bunsen burner or alcohol lamp
Pail or jar of cracked ice (or snow)

Introduction. Liquids when heated expand more than solids; for example, the mercury in a thermometer expands more than the glass bulb. Gases expand much more than liquids and, what is more remarkable, *all gases expand at about the same rate.* The expansion of gas when heated is what makes bread dough "rise" and causes the little holes in the bread. Here it is the bubbles of gas (CO_2) formed by the yeast or baking powder which expand. Why does cake dough sometimes "fall" if it is removed from the oven too soon?

The ratio between the increase in volume per degree and the volume at 0° C. is called the **volume coefficient of expansion.** Thus, if V_{100} and V_0 represent the volumes at 100° C. and 0° C., respectively, then the volume coefficient K is given by the equation

$$K = \frac{V_{100} - V_0}{100 \, V_0}.$$

If a certain quantity of gas is heated in a closed vessel so that the volume is kept constant, the pressure which the gas exerts against the walls of the vessel increases as the temperature rises. This is really what makes the gas engine work. A mixture of gas and air exploding in the closed end of the cylinder produces a very high temperature and a corresponding increase in pressure. It is this pressure which drives the piston. The ratio between the increase in pressure per

111

degree and the pressure which a gas exerts at 0° C. is called the **pressure coefficient of expansion of the gas.** Experiments show that this pressure coefficient of expansion is the same for all gases and is equal to the volume coefficient of expansion. Thus we see that this coefficient is a very important factor in all gas problems.

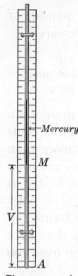

Fig. 27–1. An air thermometer.

Directions. In this experiment the apparatus is very simple. It consists of a thick-walled glass tube (about 50 cm. long) with a uniform bore of about 1.5 millimeters diameter. One end is closed. The tube contains a column of dry air about 20 to 25 centimeters long which is confined by a thread of mercury 2 or 3 centimeters long (Fig. 27–1) and is mounted on a wooden back that is graduated in millimeters. The distance AM from the closed end of the bore up to the mercury represents the volume of the air. (The volume of the air is measured in terms of the volume of a unit length of the tube.) This apparatus forms a simple, constant-pressure air thermometer and must be handled with care in order not to break the thread of mercury into two or more sections.*

Stand the air tube upright, closed end down, in a pail or jar of cracked ice (Fig. 27–2(a)). Pack the crushed ice closely about the tube so that the air column is covered with ice up to the mercury. Tap the tube with a pencil, and when the mercury index comes to a position of rest, note and record the position of the lower end of the mercury. This length AM (Fig. 27–1) represents the volume of the air at 0° C.

Now put the air tube into the top of the steam generator in

---

*In case the mercury column does get divided into sections, it can be reunited by means of a small, clean steel wire, which is pushed into the tube.

such a way as to surround the air column with steam. When the mercury ceases to rise in the tube, again note and record the position of the lower end of the mercury. This new length *AM* (Fig. 27–1) represents the volume of the air at the temperature of boiling water.

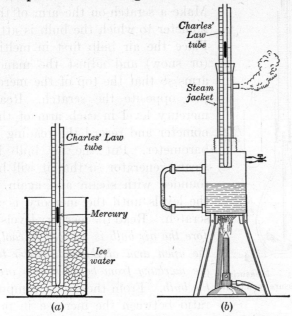

Fig. 27–2. Air thermometer in ice (*a*) and in steam (*b*).

Read the barometer and compute the temperature of the steam for the observed reading of the barometer as in Experiment 25, II.

Record your data and results in tabular form.

Results. Compute

(*a*) *the expansion of the air;*
(*b*) *the rise in temperature* (from ice to steam);
(*c*) *the expansion per degree rise in temperature;*
(*d*) *the expansion of one centimeter per degree.*

This last result is the coefficient of cubical expansion of air.

* * * *

Pressure coefficient. To determine the **pressure coefficient of expansion** of air, attach a glass bulb to a mercury

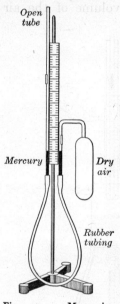

Open tube

Mercury

Dry air

Rubber tubing

Fig. 27–3. Measuring the pressure coefficient of air.

pressure gauge made of two glass tubes connected by a rubber tube (Fig. 27–3). Make a scratch on the arm of the manometer to which the bulb is attached. Place the air bulb first in melting ice (or snow) and adjust the manometer arms so that the top of the mercury is just opposite the scratch. Read the mercury level in each arm of the manometer and record the reading of the barometer. Put the air bulb in the steam generator so that it will be surrounded with steam and again adjust the levels until the mercury is at the scratch. Read the mercury levels. *Before the air bulb is allowed to cool, lower the open arm of the manometer to keep the mercury from being drawn over into the bulb.* From these data compute the ratio between the increase in pressure per degree and the pressure which the gas exerts at 0° C., that is, *the pressure coefficient of gases.*

EXPERIMENT 28

SPECIFIC HEAT OF A METAL

How many calories does 1 gram of a metal give out in cooling 1° C.?

Metal block or cylinder (such   Thermometer
   as aluminum, copper, lead,   Platform, or beam, balance
   or iron)   Set of weights
Boiler and burner   Cylindrical graduate (200 cm.³)
       Calorimeter, preferably double-walled

Introduction. Thus far we have been concerned with changes in temperature, and these we could measure with a thermometer. But very many important problems, such as the heat value of fuels, involve the *measurement of heat.* It will readily be seen that it takes *twice* as much heat to raise the temperature of a pound of water *ten* degrees as to raise a pound of water *five* degrees; and that it takes *twice* as much heat to raise the temperature of *two* pounds of water one degree as to raise *one* pound of water one degree. In short, to measure heat we must know the weight of the material heated and the number of degrees through which it is heated.

For engineering purposes in this country and in other English-speaking countries, the **heat unit** is the *British thermal unit* (B.t.u.), which is the amount of heat required to warm 1 pound of water 1 degree Fahrenheit. The heat unit that is used in almost all scientific work, however, is the *calorie.* This is the amount of heat required to warm 1 gram of water 1 degree centigrade. For example, 1 cubic foot of illuminating gas will furnish about 600 British thermal units, and a shredded wheat biscuit will supply us with energy equivalent to about 100 calories.

Different substances vary greatly in the amount of heat required to produce the same change in temperature. For example, one British thermal unit will raise the temperature of one pound of iron about 9 degrees Fahrenheit. In other words, it takes 0.11 British thermal unit to raise 1 pound of iron 1 degree Fahrenheit, and so the specific heat of iron is said to be 0.11. We can easily show that the numerical value for specific heat is the same whether we use British thermal units or calories.

Method. To measure heat we often use the **method of mixtures.** This method assumes that we can mix a hot substance with a cold substance without any loss of heat in the process. It also assumes that the heat units given out by the hot body in cooling equal the heat units absorbed by the cold body in being warmed. In carrying this out in the laboratory we use a **calorimeter,** which is usually a copper or brass vessel nickel-plated to retard radiation. Sometimes it is provided with a double wall having an air space between. In all experiments involving heat measurements the temperatures must be taken with great care (estimate to tenths of a degree), and any liquids used must be thoroughly stirred before taking the temperature.

The principle involved in this experiment is very simple. A hot mass of metal is dropped into cold water and the water absorbs the heat given out by the cooling metal. In other words,

Heat given out = heat taken in

$$m(t_m - t_{mix})X = w(t_{mix} - t_w)1$$

where m = weight of metal, t_m = temperature of metal, X = specific heat of metal, w = weight of water, t_{mix} = temperature of mixture, and t_w = temperature of cold water.

But it must also be remembered that the calorimeter which holds the water absorbs heat. Experiments show that brass (the metal commonly used for the calorimeter) absorbs about one-tenth as much heat as the same weight of water. Therefore one-tenth of the weight of the calorimeter, its **water equivalent,** is to be added to the weight of water.

Directions. It is convenient to have the metal* in the form of a block or cylinder which can be heated directly in the water of the boiler (Fig. 28–1). Weigh the metal (to 0.1 g.) and then put it into the boiler to heat.

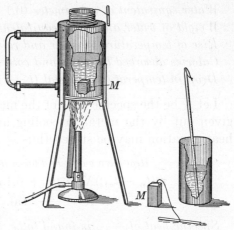

Fig. 28–1. Specific heat of a metal block *M*.

In the meantime measure out in a cylindrical graduate a certain quantity of cold water, about 200 cubic centimeters at from 5° to 10° C. Record the weight of water used, considering 1 cubic centimeter of water as equal to 1 gram. Also record the weight of the calorimeter (inner cup if used).

When the metal has reached the temperature of the boiling water, which is to be computed from the barometric reading, read carefully the temperature of the cold water. Then, by means of a thread, quickly lift the metal out of the boiler and put it into the cold water. Stir the water and take its final temperature as soon as it becomes constant.

These data should be recorded in tabular form:

Weight of metal (m)	g.
Weight of cold water (w)	g.
Weight of calorimeter (c)	g.
Temperature of metal (t_m)	° C.
Temperature of cold water (t_w)	° C.
Temperature of water and metal (t_{mix})	° C.

* If the metal for this experiment is finely divided shot, it may be heated in a dipper set in a boiler, and its temperature can be determined by placing a thermometer in the midst of the shot.

Computations. From these facts calculate the following results:

Water equivalent of calorimeter (0.1 *c*)
Weight of water and water equivalent of cal. (*w* + 0.1 *c*)
Rise of temperature of water and calorimeter ($t_{mix} - t_w$)
Calories absorbed by water and calorimeter
Drop in temperature of metal ($t_m - t_{mix}$)

Let *X* be the specific heat of the metal. Then the calories given out by the metal in cooling are $m(t_m - t_{mix})X$. The heat equation may be stated thus:

$$Heat\ given\ out = heat\ taken\ in$$
$$m(t_m - t_{mix})X = (w + 0.1\ c)(t_{mix} - t_w)$$
$$\therefore X = \text{——} cal.$$

Specific heat of —— *is found to be* —— *calories.*

The value for —— given in the table in the Appendix is —— calories.

* * * *

How hot is a red-hot ball? It will be noted that the fundamental equation for this experiment contains seven quantities. Therefore if any six of them are determined experimentally, the seventh one may be computed.

Use this method to find the temperature of a red-hot iron ball. Suspend an iron ball on an iron wire in a flame until it is red-hot (Fig. 28–2). Then plunge it into cold water in a calorimeter. Compute the number of calories received by the water and calorimeter. Knowing the weight of the ball and assuming the specific heat of iron (see Appendix), compute the temperature of the red-hot ball. What are the sources of error which render this method only approximate?

The same method can be used to determine the specific heat of a liquid by mixing it with a metal of known specific heat. If time permits, determine the specific heat of kerosene in this way.

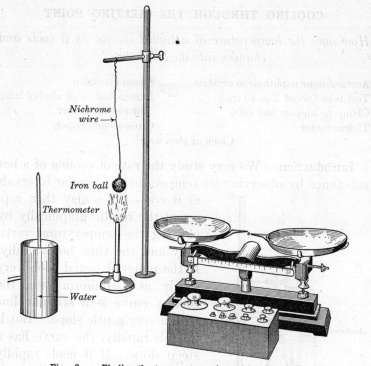

Fig. 28–2. Finding the temperature of a red-hot iron ball.

Cautions. In all heat measurements it is essential to keep the bulb of the thermometer in the liquid while reading its temperature. In the method of mixtures it is well to start the experiment with the liquid as many degrees *below* room temperature as the mixture is *above* room temperature at the end of the experiment. Why?

EXPERIMENT 29

COOLING THROUGH THE MELTING POINT

How does the temperature of a liquid change as it cools and changes into the solid state?

Acetamide or naphthalene crystals
Test tube (about 2 × 10 cm.)
Clamp to support test tube
Thermometer

Steam generator
Bunsen burner or alcohol lamp
  or electric heater
Cross-section paper

Clock or stop watch

Introduction. We may study the rate of cooling of a hot substance by observing its temperature at regular intervals as it cools. We may then rep-

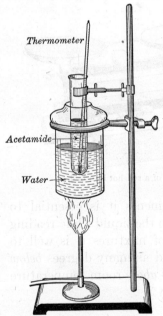

Thermometer

Acetamide

Water

Fig. 29–1. Melting crystals of acetamide.

resent the results graphically by plotting the temperatures vertically and the time horizontally. If the material tested cools very slowly at a uniform rate, the cooling curve is a straight line with a very gentle slope. But if it cools rapidly, the curve has a steep slope. If it cools rapidly at first and then gradually cools more and more slowly, the line is not straight but curves with its concave side upward. In this experiment we shall observe a decided change in the shape of the cooling curve during the process of change from liquid to solid, which indicates a new source of heat. A convenient substance to study through these temperature changes is acetamide or naphthalene.

Directions. Fill a test tube about half full of the crystals of acetamide and heat the tube in the water of the steam generator until the acetamide has reached a temperature between 95° and 100° C. (Fig. 29–1). Then remove the burner from the boiler and clamp the test tube in such a position that the thermometer is easily read as the liquid cools.

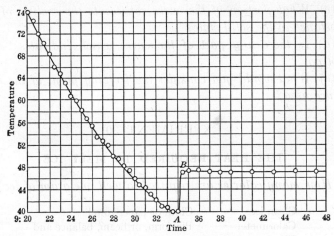

Fig. 29-2. Cooling curve of " hypo."

Without disturbing the liquid or the thermometer in any way, read and record the temperature (estimating to one-tenth of a degree) every half minute. Note when the crystals begin to form in the liquid and take the observations every minute until the solid has cooled to about 50° C.

Results. To show graphically these changes that occur during the process of cooling, we plot the results on cross-section paper, representing *temperatures* by vertical distances (5 mm. for 1°) and *times* by horizontal distances (5 mm. for 1 min.). Begin both the time scale and the temperature scale at the lower left-hand corner. Make a tiny circle or cross to indicate the position of each observation. Then draw a line passing along the course indicated by the several points located on the paper, as shown in figure 29–2.

Study this curve carefully so as to be able to answer such questions as the following:

(a) *What portion of the curve represents the cooling of the substance in the liquid state?*

(b) *What portion of the curve represents the condition during the process of crystallization?*

(c) *What portion of the curve represents the cooling of the substance in the solid state?*

(d) *Is there any part of the curve which indicates "sub-cooling"?*

(e) *What would you consider the freezing point of the substance used?*

EXPERIMENT 30

THE HEAT REQUIRED TO MELT ICE

How many calories are required to melt one gram of ice?

Clean ice	Cloth or paper towel
Calorimeter	Platform, or beam, balance and
Thermometer	set of weights
Supply of hot water (tea kettle)	

Introduction. It is a well-known fact that ice or snow absorbs heat in the process of melting. In the ice-cream freezer the broken ice in the outer bucket cools the cream to the freezing point, while the salt and ice together produce a still lower temperature, absorbing heat from the cream. In an ice refrigerator the melting of the ice is necessary for cooling the food to the proper temperature for preservation. A really good refrigerator has heat-insulating walls so that most of the heat used in melting the ice comes from the food and air inside the box and very little is conducted through the walls from the outside.

But how much heat (B.t.u.) is required to melt a pound of ice? How many calories are required to melt one gram of ice at 0° C. into water at 0° C.?   To determine this is the object of our experiment.

In attacking this problem we shall use the method of mixtures.   The heat units given out by a certain amount of warm water in cooling will be used *first* to melt the ice and *second* to raise the water which is formed from zero to the final temperature.   If each gram of ice requires X calories in changing from ice at 0° C. to water at 0° C., then i grams of ice will require iX calories.   But after the ice is melted, it becomes i grams of water at 0° C., and this water is raised to the final temperature t', which requires it' calories in addition.   This heat is supplied by w grams of water and by c grams of calorimeter (whose specific heat is about 0.1) in cooling from the initial temperature t to the final temperature t'.   This heat is equal to $(w + 0.1\ c)(t - t')$ calories. We can now make an equation as follows:

Heat absorbed by ice = heat given out by water and calorimeter
$$iX + it' = (w + 0.1\ c)(t - t')$$

From this we can solve for X, the heat of melting for ice.

Directions.   First weigh the calorimeter (only inner cup if it is a double-wall type) empty and then with about 300 grams of warm water (about 45° C.).   Break or grind up enough clean ice to fill a 150-cubic-centimeter glass with pieces less than 2 centimeters in diameter.   Stir the water in the calorimeter thoroughly and determine its temperature to a tenth of a degree.   At once add the ice quickly, taking care to wipe each piece on the cloth (why?) and not to spatter the water.   Stir the water continually.   When the temperature of the water has cooled to 10° C. or lower, stop adding ice.   Just as soon as the last piece melts, stir the water and read the temperature again with great precision.

To find out how much ice has been used, weigh the calorimeter with its water and melted ice.

We now have the following data:

Weight of calorimeter (c) . . . . g.
Weight of calorimeter + water . . . . g.
    Weight of water (w) . . . . g.
Initial temperature of water (t) . . . . ° C.
Final temperature of water (t') . . . . ° C.
Weight of calorimeter + water + ice . . . . . g.
    Weight of ice (i) . . . . g.

Computation. We may now substitute in the heat equation given above the quantities which have been determined experimentally, and may solve for X, that is, *the number of calories required to melt one gram of ice at 0° C. to water at 0° C.*

EXPERIMENT 31

THE HEAT GIVEN OUT BY CONDENSING STEAM

How many calories are given out when 1 gram of steam at 100° C. condenses into water at 100° C.?

Steam generator and burner	Thermometer
Condensed-steam trap	Platform, or beam, balance
Calorimeter	Set of weights

Introduction. Suppose we heat a certain quantity of water from 0° to 100° C. and note the time required. Then suppose we boil all the water away and note the time required for this process. We shall find that it takes about five times as long to change all the water into steam as it takes to heat the water from 0° to 100° C. Presumably the water has been receiving heat at about the same rate all the time. And the water did not get hotter than 100° C. Therefore we must conclude that it takes about five times as much heat to change it to steam as it took in when heated from 0° to 100° C. This heat which is absorbed in the process of changing water into steam is called the **heat of vaporization** or the latent heat of steam.

When the steam condenses back to water, this latent (hidden) heat of the steam is given out. It is this heat of condensation of steam which is made use of in steam heating in our houses and buildings. Steam is generated in a boiler and piped to the place where heat is wanted. It is there condensed, giving out all the heat which was absorbed in vaporizing it.

In order to determine how many calories are given out when one gram of steam at 100° C. condenses into water at 100° C., we shall run some "live steam" into cold water and observe the rise in temperature. By weighing the calorimeter and water after running in the steam, we shall be able to determine the weight of steam used. Thus it will be seen that we again use the method of mixtures. For we make an equation between the *heat units* absorbed by the calorimeter and cold water and the *heat units given out* by the steam in condensing and by the water which results from the condensed steam in cooling from 100° C. to the final temperature of the mixture. The success of this experiment depends very much on careful weighing (to 0.1 g.) and on the careful reading of the temperatures (to 0.1° C.).

Directions. Fill the boiler half full of water and start heating. Then fill the calorimeter, whose weight has already been determined, two-thirds full of cold water (about 5° C.)* and determine the weight of the water with great precision. Set up a book or wooden screen between the boiler and the calorimeter and place a thermometer in the water.

As soon as the water in the boiler begins to boil, attach the trap to the delivery tube, as shown in figure 31–1, to catch any steam which condenses in the tube. Stir the water in the calorimeter with the thermometer and read its temperature.

Then quickly put the delivery tube into the water so that its end projects under water about 2 centimeters. Continue

---

* If necessary, cool the water with bits of ice. But be sure that no ice remains unmelted when the temperature is taken.

to stir the water slowly until it gets to a temperature about as much above that of the room as the initial temperature was below it. Remove the delivery tube from the calorimeter and after stirring read the highest temperature which the water reaches.

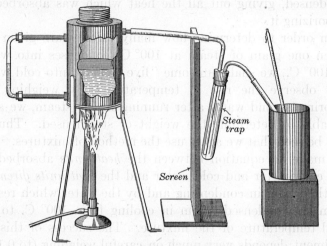

Fig. 31-1. Condensing " dry " steam in water.

Finally, as soon as convenient, weigh with great care (to 0.1 g.) the calorimeter, water, and condensed steam and compute the weight of the steam used. The temperature of the steam can best be computed from the reading of the barometer.

Record all your observations as soon as they are taken in tabular form somewhat as follows:

Weight of calorimeter (c) . . . . g.
Weight of calorimeter + water . . . . g.
Weight of water (w) . . . . g.
Initial temperature of water (t) . . . . . . ° C.
Final temperature of water (t') . . . . . . ° C.
Weight of cal. + water + steam . . . . . . g.
Weight of condensed steam (s) . . . . . . g.
Barometric pressure . . . . cm.

Computations.

(*a*) *What was the temperature of the steam?* (See Experiment 25, Part II.)

(*b*) *What is the water equivalent of the calorimeter?* (0.1 *c*)

(*c*) *How many calories have the calorimeter and water absorbed?* (*w* + 0.1 *c*)(*t'* − *t*)

(*d*) *How many calories did s grams of condensed steam give out in cooling, say from 100° C. to t' C.?* *s*(100 − *t'*)

(*e*) If we assume that each gram of steam in condensing gave out *X* calories, then *s* grams would give out *sX* calories.

(*f*) Now state in the form of an equation the heat given out and the heat absorbed. That is, substitute in the following equation :

$$Heat\ given\ out = heat\ absorbed$$
$$sX + s(100 − t') = (w + 0.1\ c)(t' − t)$$

Solve for *X*, which is the heat given up by 1 gram of steam in changing into water.

(*g*) The accepted value for the latent heat of steam is 540 calories per gram.

*   *   *   *

Compute your per cent of error.*

If time permits, make a second trial.

---

* With reasonable care it is not difficult to get a result in this experiment within 5 per cent. If the steam in the trap condenses so that water rises from the calorimeter, it is necessary to start the experiment again.

EXPERIMENT 32

DEW POINT AND RELATIVE HUMIDITY

I. *At what temperature is the air of the room saturated with the moisture present?*

II. *What is the relative humidity of the air of the room?*

Calorimeter with bright exterior surface	Tumbler of water at room temperature
Thermometer	Salt and ice

Introduction. The atmosphere always contains some moisture even though it is not visible as rain or snow. It is this moisture which makes a pitcher of ice water "sweat" during a hot day in summer and makes water drip from pipes through which cold water is flowing.

It is necessary to determine the humidity of the air in greenhouses because the plants cannot thrive if the air becomes too dry. It is well known that the air in our homes often contains less water vapor than a desert region. This too dry air rapidly absorbs moisture from the skin, nose, and throat, and prepares the way for the attack of disease germs. The excessively dry air in our houses, it is said, also leads to a waste of fuel, which is estimated at from 10 to 25 per cent. This is because a more humid atmosphere would diminish the cooling effect produced by the rapid evaporation of the perspiration from the skin and so would make us feel more comfortable at 65° F. than we do now at 70° F. To correct this condition, hospitals, public buildings, textile factories, and an increasing number of private dwellings are being "air conditioned."

How shall we measure the humidity of the atmosphere? It is possible to determine the number of grams of water vapor in one cubic meter of air. This is the absolute humidity of the atmosphere at a given temperature. Experiments show that the amount of vapor which may be present with-

128

out precipitation (rain or snow) varies with the temperature and that a rise in temperature increases rapidly the quantity of vapor required to saturate the air. This is clearly shown in Table VIII in the Appendix.

If the air is gradually cooled, a temperature will be reached at which the water vapor present will saturate the air. If now the air is still further cooled, the vapor will condense and be deposited as droplets of water. This temperature at which the air becomes saturated is called the **dew point.** Knowing the dew point, we may readily compute the **relative humidity** of the air. This is the ratio between the amount of moisture actually in the air and the amount which would be present if the air were completely saturated. For example, suppose the temperature is 20° C. and the dew point is found to be 10° C. What is the relative humidity? From the humidity tables we find that a cubic meter of saturated air at 10° C. contains 9.36 grams of water and at 20° C., 17.15 grams. Therefore the air is $\frac{9.36}{17.15}$, or 54.6 per cent, saturated.*

Directions. See that the outside of the can (Fig. 32–1) is bright. Half fill the vessel with water at room temperature. Gradually cool this water by adding chips of ice (and salt if needed) and stir constantly with the thermometer. Carefully watch the lower part of the can for the first signs of moisture. Just as soon as a faint mist appears, read the temperature. One method of determining when moisture appears on the surface of the can is to place it on a printed page and observe the reflection of the letters on the polished surface of the can. The letters appear blurred if there is even a slight quantity of moisture on the polished surface. Avoid breathing on the can by setting a sheet of glass in front of the can.

---

* For a more complete discussion of humidity and its measurement, see Bureau of Standards Circular No. 55, *Measurements for the Household;* U. S. Government Printing Office, Washington, D. C.

Remove from the water any of the ice which is unmelted. Slowly add a little warm water to the calorimeter until the mist begins to disappear. Read carefully the temperature of the water.

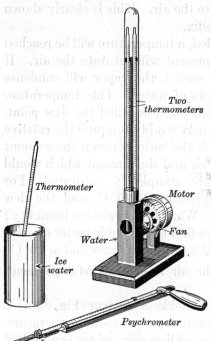

The reading of the thermometer as you cooled the water was a bit too low since one cannot detect the condensation the very instant it appears. And likewise, the temperature in the second case, as the water was being warmed, was a trifle too high. By taking the average of these readings, we can obtain very nearly the true dew point.

Repeat this experiment several times and take the mean of the average values for the dew point.

Fig. 32-1. Various instruments for determining relative humidity.

Record the temperature of the air in the room, the out-of-door temperature, and the kind of weather.

Tabulate your observations.

Computation. From the humidity tables, find the weight of water vapor in one cubic meter of saturated air at the dew point. Also find the weight of water vapor which would saturate one cubic meter of air at room temperature. Finally, *determine the per cent of relative humidity.*

* * * *

Use of wet- and dry-bulb thermometers. To determine the relative humidity by the wet- and dry-bulb thermometers, one can improvise this type of hygrometer (Fig. 32–1) from two Fahrenheit thermometers. Wrap some cotton gauze around the bulb of one thermometer and let the lower end of this wick dip into a glass of water. When the readings of the two thermometers have become stationary, read each thermometer. The wet-bulb thermometer will read lower than the dry-bulb thermometer on account of the evaporation of water from the gauze around the bulb surface. Keep the air in motion around the thermometer bulbs by whirling the thermometers (sling psychrometer) or blowing air with a tiny electric fan. Determine the difference in temperature readings in the two thermometers and use Table IX in the Appendix to find the *relative humidity*.

EXPERIMENT 33

HEAT OF COMBUSTION OF GAS

How many B.t.u. are produced when 1 cubic foot of gas is burned in a Bunsen burner?

Gas calorimeter (Junker)	Watch
Gas-flow gauge (Thorpe)	2 Thermometers (0.1° C.)
Bunsen burner	Can for measuring water
	Scales and weights

Introduction. The " heat of combustion," *i.e.*, the B.t.u. derived per cubic foot of gas burned, is to be found in this experiment for ordinary artificial or natural gas. A gas calorimeter of the Junker type is supplied with a continuous flow of water. The hot gases resulting from the flame pass out through pipes surrounded with water, where they give up their heat. The rate of gas flow is measured by a gauge that indicates directly the number of "cubic feet per hour" which is being consumed. The heat produced is equal to the product of the quantity of water flowing through the calorimeter per hour and the rise of temperature indicated by the two thermometers placed in the outflowing and inflowing stream of water (Fig. 33–1).

Directions. Connect the calorimeter with the water reservoir so that a small but steady stream of water enters the bottom of the calorimeter and flows out at the top. Then adjust the Bunsen burner until, when burning low, the air supply is sufficient to make it burn with a rustling sound

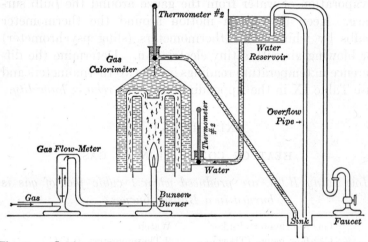

Fig. 33–1. Continuous-flow calorimeter used to measure the heat of combustion of gas.

and a blue flame without white in it. Put the burner under the calorimeter, but *not* before the water is started. Why not? Keep the gas current constant at some chosen point on the gauge, say 4 or 5 cubic feet per hour. Note the readings of the inlet and outlet thermometers of the calorimeter. Adjust the flow of water until the temperature of the outflowing water is about as much above the temperature of the room as that of the inflowing water is below the temperature of the room. When these temperatures have become steady, read both thermometers to one-tenth of a degree. At the same time catch the outflowing water in a can (previously weighed) for a measured time interval —

time enough nearly to fill the can. Weigh the water in the
can and compute the quantity of water flowing through the
calorimeter per hour.

Then compute the heat received (in B.t.u.) by this water
per hour. Finally, calculate the heat of combustion of the
gas in B.t.u. per cubic foot.

Data and Computations

Reading of gas gauge	cu. ft. per hr.
Temperature of inflowing water	° C., ° F.
Temperature of outflowing water	° C., ° F.
Weight of empty can	g.
Weight of can and water	g.
Weight of water	lbs.
Time required to catch water	min.
Weight of water flowing through calorimeter per hour	lbs.
B.t.u. absorbed by water per hour	
B.t.u. produced by burning 1 cubic foot of gas . . .	

Question. *What are the most likely sources of error in
this experiment?   Give your reasons.*

*   *   *   *

Efficiency of a gas stove. The consumer is interested in
the ratio of the heat units which he actually uses, say in
boiling water, to the heat of combustion of the gas used.
In other words, he wants to know the thermal efficiency of his
gas stove and kettle.

Since we do so much of our housework nowadays by electricity, we shall be interested in determining the cost of
heating water by a gas stove, and later (Experiment 49)
we can compare this with the cost of doing the same thing
by electricity.

To measure the gas consumed in our experiment, we shall
need to get acquainted with a commercial gas meter. The
ordinary household meter has three dials (Fig. 33–2), each
with an index hand. The dial at the left is labeled "100
THOUSAND," which means that for one complete revolution

of the hand 100,000 cubic feet of gas have passed through the meter. The next dial is marked "10 THOUSAND," and the right-hand dial "1 THOUSAND." In commercial work these circles are read once a month, and the gas bill is made out according to the number of hundred cubic feet. For testing purposes there is a small fourth dial

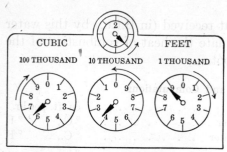

Fig. 33-2.   Gas meter reads 63,800.

above these three dials, and one complete revolution of its index hand records only 2 cubic feet of gas. By using this little dial we can measure the gas consumed to one-tenth of a cubic foot.

Directions.* Connect the gas meter on the inlet side with a gas cock and attach the gas stove to the other side (Fig. 33-3). Let about a quarter of a cubic foot of gas pass

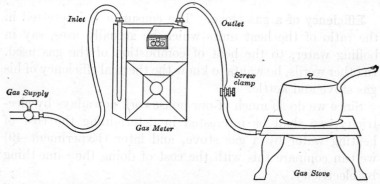

Fig. 33-3.   How much gas is needed to boil water?

through the meter before lighting the stove. *Why?* Light the gas stove and let it burn until the index hand on the

* This experiment may be performed at home with a gas-range burner and your own gas meter and teakettle.

2-cubic-foot dial has reached some convenient point for reading. Then turn off the gas.

Measure out carefully one quart of water and pour it into a four-quart saucepan. Get the temperature of the water as near 60° F. as possible. Place the pan of water upon the stove and start heating. Note the initial reading of the gas meter and the time of starting. Allow the heating to continue until the water begins to boil rapidly with steam coming from the bottom. Then turn off the gas and record the time of stopping and the amount of gas consumed.

Record your data and computed results in tabular form.

Computation.

(a) *How many cubic feet of gas were consumed in the heating?* (Express the volume to 0.1 cu. ft.)

(b) *How many British thermal units were absorbed by the water?* (1 qt. of water weighs 2.08 lbs.)

(c) *How many heat units were produced by the gas consumed?* (Assume that 1 cu. ft. of gas gives 540 B.t.u. unless otherwise directed.*)

(d) *What per cent of the total heat produced by the burning of the gas was used in heating the water?* (This result is the thermal efficiency of the stove and kettle.)

If time permits, repeat this experiment with a cover on the saucepan, and compute the efficiency and cost. *Which is the more economical way of heating water? Why?*

* It is suggested that you get from your local gas company their B.t.u. rating.

EXPERIMENT 34

MECHANICAL EQUIVALENT OF HEAT

How many gram-meters of work are required to heat one gram of water one degree centigrade?

Frictional machine or Jouler	Thermometer (0.1° C.)
Handwheel	Scales and weights

Introduction. In this experiment the friction is produced between two brass cones which are ground to fit very nicely. The inner cone contains the water to be heated and is held

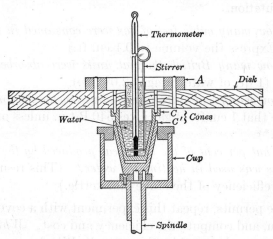

Fig. 34-1. Cross section of the Jouler.

more or less stationary. The outer cone is rotated by a spindle which, in turn, is made to revolve by means of a belt passing around a handwheel. A counting device records the number of revolutions of the spindle. The inner cone is prevented from revolving by means of a wooden grooved disk which has a string attached to its circumference. A known weight W is attached to the other end of the string, which passes over a fixed grooved pulley (Fig. 34-1).

136

The *work done* in overcoming friction between the two cones is the same as would have been done if the outer cone had been fixed and the inner cone revolved by the weight W falling through a distance equal to the circumference of the groove of the wooden disk times the number of revolutions of the spindle.   (Work = $W \times \pi$ diam. $\times$ revol.).

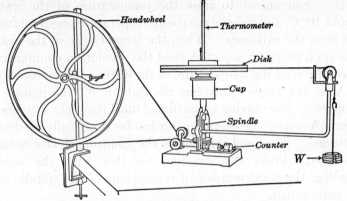

Fig. 34-2.   Measuring the heat produced by friction.

The *heat generated* is used not only to raise the temperature of the water in the cones, but also to raise the temperature of the cones and stirrer.   Assuming the specific heat of the metal used in the construction of the cones to be 0.095, we can compute the water equivalent of the cones and stirrer. Then, neglecting the heat which has escaped by radiation, conduction, and convection, we can calculate the total number of calories produced.

Directions.   First the cones and the stirrer are weighed together.   Then the inner cone is filled to about 1 cm. from its top with water about 10° below the temperature of the room. Then the weight of the water is determined.   The cones are now placed in position in the Jouler and everything arranged in working order (Fig. 34-2).   One observer should give attention to stirring the water in the cone and to reading its temperature.   It will require some care on the part of the second observer to maintain the proper rate of rotation by means of the handwheel. A uniform rate of turning is not required, but it is necessary that the weight W should be suspended by the friction alone. The handwheel must be turned just fast enough to raise the weight W so that the string supporting W is tangential to the edge of the disk.

It is convenient to raise the temperature of the water about 10° C. and to have the room temperature about midway between the extremes. When the temperature of the water has been properly adjusted, read the revolution counter and carefully read the temperature of the water. Begin rotating.

After the temperature has risen about 8°, the motion is stopped. The stirring is continued until the highest temperature shown by the thermometer has been carefully read and recorded. The final reading of the counting device is also observed. From this reading, together with the initial reading, the total number of revolutions of the spindle can be determined.

Data

Weight of cones and stirrer . . . . . . g.
Weight of cones, stirrer, and water . . . g.
        Weight of water . . . . g.
Room temperature . . . . ° C.
Reading of counter at start . . . . . .
Temperature of water at start . . . . . ° C.
Reading of counter at finish . . . . . .
Highest temperature of water . . . . ° C.
Suspended weight . . . . g.
Diameter of disk . . . . cm.

Computations

Water equivalent of cones and stirrer . . g.
Rise of temperature . . . . ° C.
    Heat units generated . . . . . . g.-cal.
Number of revolutions . . . .
Circumference of the disk . . . . . . m.
    Work done by friction . . . . . g.-m.
Therefore 1 gram-calorie = ... g.-m. of work

SECOND HALF YEAR

MAGNETISM AND ELECTRICITY

BLOCK V. FUNDAMENTALS OF MAGNETISM AND ELECTRICITY

Suggestive Questions

1. *What is the essential difference between a dry cell and a storage cell?*

2. *What appliances make use of permanent magnets?*

3. *Why is an electromagnet better for a hoist than a permanent magnet?*

4. *Why is the hot resistance of a tungsten lamp more important than its cold resistance?*

5. *When a 25-watt lamp is connected in parallel with a 50-watt lamp, how does the current divide?*

6. *If two lamps (25-watt and 50-watt) are connected in series, what is the relation between the currents in each?*

7. *What would happen if you connected a 6-volt lamp to a 115-volt line?*

8. *Why are electric cables made of copper and not of iron?*

9. *When a lamp "burns out" in a house, why don't the other lamps go out too?*

10. *Why are the coils of a resistance box made of manganin wire instead of iron?*

11. *What two units are used in describing an incandescent lamp?*

12. *Why are fuses inserted in every house-lighting circuit?*

13. *What is the real function of a lightning rod placed on the chimney of a dwelling house?*

14. *Will an electric toaster use more current before or after it becomes hot?*

EXPERIMENT 35

MAGNETIC LINES OF FORCE

I. *What is the direction of the magnetic lines of force about a bar magnet?*

II. *What is the nature of the magnetic field about certain combinations of magnets?*

Two cobalt-steel bar magnets
  (15 cm. × 19 mm. × 6 mm.)
Soft-iron washer (2.2 cm. diam.)
Two strips of wood (30 × 1 × 0.6 cm.)
Tracing compass (1.0 cm.)

Sheet of white paper
Sheet of cardboard
Brass thumb tacks
Iron filings in carton with
  sifter top

Introduction. Although we do not know just what magnetism is, some of our commonest mechanical devices depend upon it for their usefulness. For instance, it is probable that there are in commercial use at the present time at least two hundred million permanent magnets. Besides the straight magnets used in mariners' and surveyors' compasses, we have U-shaped magnets in various electric meters, in every telephone receiver, and in telephone magnetos. Every motorcycle and airplane carries permanent magnets in its magneto.

We can learn a great deal about the action of magnets by plotting what Faraday called **magnetic lines of force.** *A line of magnetic force may be defined as a line which indicates at its every point the direction in which a north-seeking pole is urged by the attractions and repulsions of all the poles in the neighborhood.* Every magnet has its property of attracting iron filings more or less definitely concentrated in two or more spots, called **poles.** Also, when the magnet is free to turn, it will set itself with one pole toward the north (the

140

north-seeking pole) and the other toward the south (the south-seeking pole).   Experiments show that

like poles repel each other,
unlike poles attract each other;

also that these forces between magnetic poles vary inversely as the square of the distance between the poles.

Directions.   *Magnetic lines about a bar magnet.*   With the aid of the small tracing compass, turn the sheet of paper so that its longer edges are parallel to the compass needle, and then fasten the paper to the table or drawing board with thumb tacks. (In orienting the paper be sure that the permanent magnets are several feet away.)   In-dicate by an arrow in the corner of the paper the north and south di-rection.   Lay the mag-net on the paper near the middle so that its axis lies nearly north and south with the *S*-pole toward the north (Fig. 35–1). Trace with

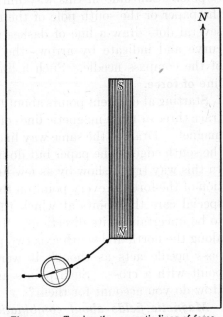

Fig. 35–1.   Tracing the magnetic lines of force.

a sharp, hard pencil the outline of the magnet and mark the position of its poles with the letters *N* and *S*.

Make a dot near one corner of the north-seeking end of the magnet.   Place the tracing compass on the paper beside the magnet in such a way that the *S*-pole of the compass needle lies as nearly as possible right over the dot which serves as a

starting point.   Then mark with a pencil the position of the
N-pole of the compass needle (Fig. 35–1).   (If the tracing
compass is the Hahn type with four notches in the rim, place
the compass so that one notch is directly over the dot and
then turn the compass around this point until the needle
stands exactly over the line on the compass base.)   Move
the compass in the direction in which its N-pole points until
the S-pole lies exactly over the mark which has just been
made.   Make a third dot to indicate the position of the
N-pole.   Continue in this way until you reach the edge of
the paper or the south pole of the magnet.   Through these
several dots draw a line of dashes in the form of a smooth
curve and indicate by arrows the direction of the N-pole
of the compass needle.   Such a line represents a **magnetic
line of force.**

Starting at different points about the N-pole of the magnet,
trace three or more magnetic lines of force on each side of the
magnet.   Draw in the same way lines of force which start on
the south edge of the paper but do not hit the magnet at all.
In this way try to show by as few lines as possible the direction of the force at every point on the paper.   Examine with
special care the points at which the compass needle seems
to be uncertain in its directions.   It will be possible to find
along the north and south axis two points at which the compass needle acts as though it were "dead."   Mark each
point with a cross.   Such points are called **neutral points.**
How do you account for them?

Magnetic fields about combinations of magnets.   Place
two bar magnets in line with each other and with the unlike

poles about 10 cm. apart, as shown
in figure 35–2.   Put some strips
of wood alongside to support the

Fig. 35–2.   N and S poles.

sheet of cardboard.   Sprinkle iron filings evenly over the
cardboard and tap lightly so as to shake the filings about a
little.   They will arrange themselves in regular lines of mag-

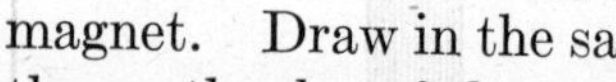

netic force since each filing gets slightly magnetized by the bar magnets and sets itself in the direction of a tiny compass needle. Draw in your notebook a sketch (reduced in size) of the magnets and the lines of force about and between them.

If time permits, remove the iron filings from the cardboard and place a soft-iron washer in the magnetic field between the north and south poles of the two

Fig. 35-3.   Soft-iron ring *W* in a magnetic field.

permanent magnets as shown in figure 35-3. Replace the sheet of cardboard and again sprinkle the iron filings over it and tap as before. Draw a sketch of this in your notebook, indicating by outlines the iron filings and the lines of magnetic force. Explain the difference in the arrangement of the lines of magnetic force caused by the introduction of the soft-iron washer.

* * * *

Determining the pole-strength of a magnet. To *magnetize* a bar of hardened steel, place it in the center of a magnetizing coil (Fig. 35-4) and momentarily close the circuit by pressing the key. When we remove the steel from the

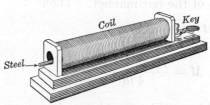

coil, we find that it is a bar magnet. To *demagnetize* the steel bar, place the magnet inside the coil and, while holding the key depressed, slowly withdraw the magnet from the coil to a dis-

Fig. 35-4.   A hardened-steel bar can be magnetized in a coil with d-c. or a-c.

tance of 2 or 3 feet from it. Reverse the magnet end for end and repeat the process.

The pole strength of a magnet is measured in units which may be defined as follows: Two equal poles which attract or repel each other with a force of one dyne* when placed one centimeter apart are called **unit poles**. When any two magnetic poles of strengths M_1 and M_2 are d centimeters apart, they act on each other with a force of $\dfrac{M_1 M_2}{d^2}$ dynes. That is,

$$f(\text{dynes}) = \frac{M_1 M_2}{d^2}.$$

The lines of magnetic force which have been traced in the first part of this experiment are the result of the bar magnet's

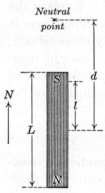

Fig. 35–5. Finding the pole strength of magnet NS.

field and of the earth's field. At the so-called "neutral points" the resultants of these forces are equal in magnitude and opposite in direction. If the earth's field strength † is known, then the field due to the bar magnet may be calculated in terms of its pole strength as follows: In figure 35–5 we let the length of the bar magnet be L and the distance between its poles $2\,l$. Let m be the pole strength of the exploring compass and M the pole strength of the bar magnet. Let d be the distance from the "neutral point" to the midpoint of the bar magnet. Then

$$mH + \frac{mM}{(d+l)^2} = \frac{mM}{(d-l)^2}$$

and

$$M = \frac{H(d^2 - l^2)^2}{4\,ld}.$$

---

* A dyne is a very small unit of force which is equal to $\frac{1}{980}$ of a gram, or 0.00102 gram.

† The earth's field strength H is the horizontal force in dynes exerted by the earth on a unit pole. In the vicinity of Boston, H is about 0.166 dyne.

EXPERIMENT 36

THE VOLTAIC CELL

I. *How is an electric current generated by chemical action?*

II. *How does the voltage of a cell depend upon the size and nature of the electrodes?*

Voltmeter (0 − 3) or galvanometer with 1000-ohm coil
Simple voltaic cell with various electrodes, such as zinc, copper, carbon, and lead

Sulfuric acid (diluted 1 to 20)
Sodium bichromate crystals
Connecting wires

Introduction. Electric currents were first produced by chemical action about the year 1800 by an Italian scientist named Volta. Today we still use this method for generating small electric currents for intermittent use. The so-called dry cell is the voltaic cell which is used for such purposes as ringing door bells and for flash lights.

When almost any two conductors are placed in a solution which acts on one of them more than on the other, a difference in potential (*i.e.*, a difference in electrical condition) is produced between the two conductors. When they are joined by a wire, an electric current flows from one to the other, as shown by certain magnetic effects. When a strip of copper and a strip of zinc are placed in dilute sulfuric acid, we have a simple voltaic cell. It is customary to call the plate which is attacked less by the solution the **positive** (+) **electrode** (the copper) and the other the **negative** (−) **electrode** (the zinc).*

We may easily detect which electrode of a cell is positive by connecting it with a voltmeter. This is merely a high-

---

* It is customary to assume that the current flows from the positive to the negative electrode through a wire which joins the two plates. But we now know that the electrons actually flow from the negative to the positive electrode in the wire. We shall, however, follow the conventional system of nomenclature about the direction of electric currents except when we are dealing with a stream of electrons.

145

resistance d'Arsonval galvanometer designed to measure voltage, or the difference of potential, directly. The electrode which is connected to the positive (+) terminal of the voltmeter is the positive electrode, that is, provided the needle of the instrument moves across the scale to the right as intended by the manufacturers.

Directions. I. *Action of dilute sulfuric acid on copper and zinc.* (1) *Open circuit.* Fill a tumbler about three-fourths full of dilute sulfuric acid (1 to 20) and put a strip of copper and a strip of zinc into the acid in such a way as to avoid all metallic connections between the strips. Observe for a few minutes the action of the acid on each strip and then *record just what is seen on the surface of each metal.* (The bubbles are hydrogen.)

(2) *Closed circuit.* Connect the tops of the strips with short copper wire and notice what change, if any, takes place on the surface of each metal. *Record the results.*

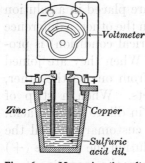

Fig. 36–1. Measuring the voltage of a voltaic cell.

(3) *Amalgamated zinc.* Replace the ordinary zinc which has just been used by an amalgamated zinc plate or rod (*i.e.,* zinc which has been dipped in mercury and rubbed until it is covered with a smooth coating of mercury). Repeat the experiment with the circuit open and closed and *record any differences which are observed in the action.*

(4) *Polarization.* It will be observed (Fig. 36–1) that the voltage of the cell does not remain steady but gradually decreases. This is caused by the accumulation of hydrogen upon the copper plate and is called **polarization.** We can hasten the process by short-circuiting the cell for half a minute with a stout, short, copper wire. When the wire is removed, *read and record the voltage.* Stir a few crystals

of sodium bichromate into the acid solution and watch the voltmeter as the crystals dissolve. (These crystals oxidize the hydrogen.) *Record the effect of the oxidizing agent on the voltage.*

II. *Effect of size of cell.* Connect a simple cell, such as the one shown in figure 36–2, with a low-reading voltmeter.* Note the deflection of the needle. Then move

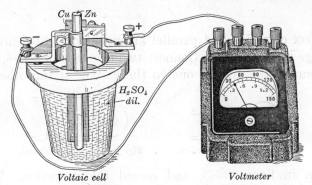

Voltaic cell   Voltmeter

Fig. 36–2.   Effect of size of cell on its voltage.

the plates as far apart as possible in the jar and again note and record the deflection. Finally lift the plates almost out of the liquids and record the deflection.

What effect does the distance between the plates and the immersed area of the plates seem to have on the electromotive force of a cell?

III. *Effect of using different metals.* Note the amount of the deflection caused by the zinc-copper cell. Remove the copper plate, insert a carbon plate or rod, and again note the direction and amount of the deflection. If the deflection is in the same direction as above, it shows that the carbon is positive (+) with respect to zinc; but if it is in the opposite direction, then the zinc is positive (+)

* In case a direct-reading voltmeter is not available for this experiment, it is possible to substitute a simple galvanometer in series with a high-resistance coil (about 1000 ohms). When used with such a high-resistance coil, the deflections are almost proportional to the voltage applied.

with respect to the carbon. In this case reverse the connections and measure the voltage. In the same way test the following pairs of metals as electrodes: zinc-lead, lead-copper, and lead-carbon.

(*a*) *Which pair gives the highest voltage?*

(*b*) *Which metal among those investigated is positive with respect to some metals and negative with respect to others?*

*   *   *   *

Effect of series and parallel arrangement. Measure the voltage of a dry cell. Connect two dry cells in series, that is, connect the zinc of one to the carbon of the other, as

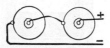 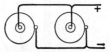

Fig. 36–3.   Cells in series.   Fig. 36–4.   Cells in parallel.

shown in figure 36–3, and record the deflection. Then connect the same cells in parallel, that is, zinc to zinc and copper to copper, as shown in figure 36–4, and again read and record the deflection.

Compare these results with the deflection of a single cell.

(*a*) *What is the effect of the series arrangement on the voltage?*

(*b*) *What is the effect of the parallel arrangement on the voltage?*

EXPERIMENT 37

MEASUREMENT OF RESISTANCE BY VOLTMETER–AMMETER METHOD. OHM'S LAW

I. *How can we measure the resistance of a wire by means of a voltmeter and an ammeter?*

II. *How does the resistance of a wire depend upon its length, cross section, and material?*

Voltmeter (0 – 15)
Ammeter (0 – 3)
Battery (6-volt storage or 5 dry cells)

4 coils of wire of varying lengths, cross section, and material *
Key or switch

Introduction. In order to compute the current drawn by an electrical appliance, we must know the electromotive force applied and the resistance of the appliance. For example, suppose we use a 6-volt battery to light a 10-ohm lamp. Then the current will be 0.6 ampere. But if we use a 20-ohm lamp, the current will be only 0.3 ampere. The general law (Ohm's) is as follows:

$$\text{Current (amperes)} = \frac{\text{electromotive force (volts)}}{\text{resistance (ohms)}}.$$

In this experiment we shall use Ohm's Law to determine the resistance of various wires by measuring the difference of potential (volts) between the ends of each wire and the current through the wire. The proper arrangement of the wire, the voltmeter, and the ammeter is shown in figure 37–1. It will be noted that the ammeter is inserted in the circuit with the wire and that the voltmeter is connected around the wire. Of course, the instruments must be connected with due regard to the + and − terminals. It will be

---

* It is suggested that the coils be made as follows: *A*, 50 cm. No. 30 G.S. or chromel wire; *B*, 200 cm. No. 30 G.S. wire; *C*, 200 cm. No. 27 G.S. wire; and *D*, 2000 cm. No. 30 copper wire. These coils should be wound non-inductively.

helpful to think of the electric current as an invisible fluid which flows from the + terminal of the battery (when the

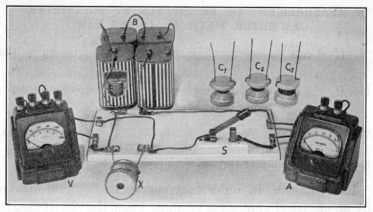

Fig. 37-1.　Measuring resistance X by means of a voltmeter V and an ammeter A.

switch is closed) into the + terminal of the ammeter, then from the − terminal of the ammeter into the coil of wire, and finally returns again to the battery.　The + terminal of the voltmeter is connected with the terminal of the coil at which the current enters, and the − terminal of the voltmeter is connected to the terminal of the coil at which

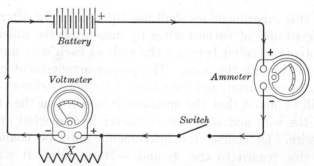

Fig. 37-2.　Diagram of connections for voltmeter-ammeter method.

the current leaves.　This is all explained more clearly and briefly in the wiring diagram (Fig. 37-2).

Directions. Set up the apparatus as shown in the diagram with coil A as the unknown resistance to be measured. The number of dry cells in the battery to be used depends upon the resistance of the coil. It is suggested that you make two trials with each coil, first using 4 cells (6 volts) and then 5 cells (7.5 volts) if time permits.

Data. It is also suggested that you record your data in tabular form somewhat as follows:

COIL	BATTERY	CURRENT (AMPERES)	VOLTAGE (VOLTS)	RESISTANCE (OHMS) $\left(R = \dfrac{E}{I}\right)$
A, 50 cm. No. 30 G.S.	4 cells			
	5 cells			
B, 200 cm. No. 30 G.S.	4 cells			
	5 cells			
C, 200 cm. No. 27 G.S.	4 cells			
	5 cells			
D, 2000 cm. No. 30 Cu.	4 cells			
	5 cells			

Results. (1) *How do coils A and B compare in length? How do their resistances compare? What is the relation between the resistances of two similar wires which vary in length?*

(2) Look up in the Appendix the area of cross section of the two wires used in coils B and C. *What is the ratio of these cross-section areas? What is the ratio of the resistances of these two coils? What is the relation between the resistances of two wires of the same length and material but different cross section?*

(3) The coil D is made of copper wire. *Compute the resistance of 200 centimeters of No. 30 copper wire. Compare the resistances of 200 cm. of No. 30 German Silver (or the chrome-alloy used) and copper.*

EXPERIMENT 38

VOLTAGE BETWEEN POINTS OF A CONDUCTOR

I. *When a steady current is flowing along a conductor, how does the voltage between two points vary with the resistance?*

II. *When the resistance remains fixed, how does the voltage depend upon the current?*

Ammeter (0 — 3 amp.)	Storage battery (6 volts)
Voltmeter (0 — 3 volts)	Variable rheostat
Slide-wire bridge (1 meter)	Switch

Introduction. When a generator is used to furnish electricity to some distant point, it is found that the voltage at the generator is higher than that at the other end of the line. This "drop in voltage" is due to voltage needed to send the current through the line. In this experiment we shall learn how this drop in voltage depends on the resistance of the line and the current flowing in the line.

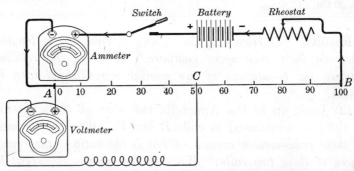

Fig. 38–1. Measuring the voltage drop along a conductor.

Directions. I. *Voltage across equal resistances.* Connect a high-resistance wire one meter long in series with a low-reading ammeter, an adjustable rheostat, and a source of steady current, such as a battery of storage cells, as shown in figure 38–1. Make the connections such that the current enters at the end marked 0 and adjust the resistance so that the current is one ampere. Touch the + terminal of the voltmeter to the 0 terminal of the wire and touch the other terminal firmly against the wire at a point just 10 centimeters from the 0 terminal. Read the voltmeter carefully and record this as the **potential difference,** or **voltage,** between the ends of this 10-centimeter length of wire. In the same way, keeping the current constant, measure the voltage from 10 to 20, 20 to 30, etc., *i.e.,* for each 10-centimeter length along the wire. Each time open the switch. If we assume that the wire is of uniform cross section, how do the resistances of equal lengths compare? *What conclusion can you draw regarding the voltage across equal resistances carrying the same current?*

II. *Voltage across varying resistances.* Connect the + terminal of the voltmeter to the 0 end of the wire, place the other terminal successively at 10, 20, 30 centimeters, etc., and record the voltage for each case. How does the resistance of 20 centimeters of wire compare with the resistance of 10 centimeters? How does the voltage across 20 centimeters of wire compare with that across 10 centimeters? Compare the resistances and voltages for 40-centimeter and 80-centimeter lengths in the same way.

When the current is kept constant in a conductor, how does the voltage depend on the resistance?

III. *Effect of varying current on voltage.* Measure the voltage across 50 centimeters of wire when the current is 0.5 ampere, 1.0 ampere, then 1.5, 2.0, 2.5, and 3.0 amperes.

How does the voltage across any given conductor vary with the current flowing?

Upon what two factors does the voltage across any given conductor depend?

Compute the resistance (ohms) of 10 centimeters of the high-resistance wire used.

* * * *

Voltage drop in a line. Connect four 25-watt lamps in parallel, as shown in figure 38–2. Between each lamp and the next, use about 3 meters of No. 18 nichrome wire which is coiled up rather tightly to save space. Connect this

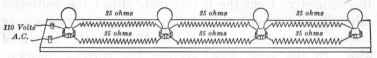

Fig. 38–2.   Voltage drop in a line depends upon the resistance and the current.

circuit with a 110-volt line and note the brightness of the lamps. *Why is the last lamp so dim?* Turn off the lamps, beginning with the one nearest the line. *How is the brightness of the last lamp changed? Why? What is the effect of using 75-watt lamps instead of 25-watt lamps?* With a voltmeter measure the voltage at each lamp socket. *How do you account for the voltage drop in the line?*

EXPERIMENT 39

MEASUREMENT OF ELECTROMOTIVE FORCE BY POTENTIOMETER

I. *How can an unknown electromotive force be compared with that of a standard cell?*

II. *What is the electromotive force of an Edison cell? Of a Daniell cell?*

Potentiometer (simple form)   Daniell cell
Lead storage cell   Edison storage cell
D'Arsonval galvanometer with   Dry cell
   shunt   Key

Introduction. The usual method of measuring voltage is by means of a high-resistance galvanometer, known as a voltmeter. But this instrument is often calibrated by means of a potentiometer. This apparatus enables one to measure an unknown voltage in terms of the voltage of a standard cell (such as the Weston Cell) which has been very accurately measured and adopted as a legal standard. Moreover, the potentiometer has a great advantage in that no current is drawn from the source of potential being measured.

In the form of potentiometer used in this experiment (Fig. 39–1) we have a high resistance ABC, through which a storage cell E causes a small, steady current to flow. The

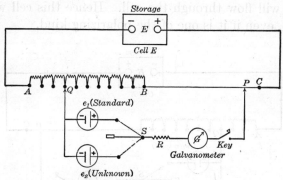

Fig. 39-1.   Diagram of a simple form of potentiometer.

voltage drop along the path of the current is proportional to the resistance passed over $(v = ir)$. Now suppose the terminals of a standard cell e_1 are connected in series with a sensitive galvanometer and key to the points P and Q on the resistance in such a way that *the voltage of the cell is opposed to the potential drop between these points*. Suppose also that the resistance between P and Q is so adjusted that no current flows through the galvanometer. Then the voltage drop (ir) through that part of the resistance exactly equals the e.m.f. produced by the cell e_1.

If now an unknown electromotive force e_2 is substituted for the standard cell e_1, new points of balance will be found along the resistance ABC; as, for example, $P'Q'$ with a resistance r'. Then the electromotive force e_2 is equal to the voltage drop ir'. By combining these two equations we have

$$\frac{e_1}{e_2} = \frac{ir}{ir'} \text{ and } e_2 = \frac{e_1 r'}{r}.$$

In this type of potentiometer (Fig. 39–2) we have ten 10-ohm coils AB connected in series with one another and with a 10-ohm slide wire BC 50 centimeters long.   A resistance R is inserted in the cell circuit so that no appreciable current will flow through the cell.   Hence this cell will not polarize, even if it is one of the polarizing kind.

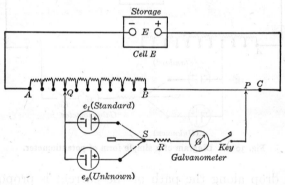

Fig. 39–1 (*repeated*).   Diagram of a simple form of potentiometer.

Directions.   Connect the potentiometer terminals A and C to a lead storage cell E which gives an e.m.f. of about 2 volts.   It will be seen that the voltage of the storage cell E must always be greater than that of the cells to be tested.   Place a fresh flashlight dry cell e_1 between the copper clips and use this as a standard cell.   Assume its e.m.f. to be 1.50 volts.   Connect the negative terminal (zinc) of the dry cell to such a binding post as Q between A and B so that the movable contact P (connected with the positive terminal of the dry cell) will be located on the wire between B and C when no current flows through the shunted galvanometer G.   When the approximate position of P has been found, remove the galvanometer shunt (not shown) and determine the precise position of P.

Record the resistance between Q and B and also the distance between B and P. Then compute the total resistance between Q and P. From this compute the current I.

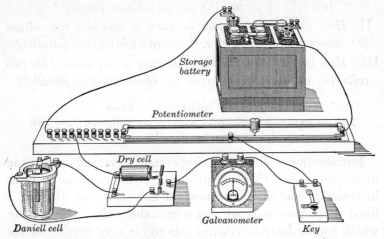

Fig. 39–2. A simple form of potentiometer for measuring e.m.f.

Turn the switch S so as to use the cell e_2, which is the cell of unknown e.m.f., and repeat the operation of finding the points Q' and P' where the galvanometer shows no current. Then record the resistance $Q'B$ and the distance BP' and compute the total resistance $Q'P'$. Now, from the equation given above, compute the e.m.f. of the unknown cell.

In this way measure the e.m.f. of an Edison storage cell and a Daniell cell. Tabulate your data and results.

Results. *Compare these results with voltages obtained with a direct-reading voltmeter. Why should we expect the potentiometer method to give slightly higher values than the voltmeter?*

RESISTORS IN SERIES AND IN PARALLEL

I. *How should an ammeter be used to measure current (a) in two coils in series, (b) in two coils in parallel?*

II. *How should a voltmeter be used to measure the voltage (a) across two coils in series, (b) across two coils in parallel?*

III. *How can we compute the resistance (a) of each of the two coils, (b) of two coils in series, (c) of two coils in parallel?*

110-volt d-c. line or storage battery	Fuses
2 Resistors of G.S. or nichrome wire *	Voltmeter (0 — 150)
Ammeter (0 — 15)	

Introduction. The most important electrical measuring instruments are the voltmeter and the ammeter. Each instrument contains a d'Arsonval galvanometer, that is, a fixed permanent magnet and a movable coil. The current which can be introduced into this coil is very small, but the deflections of the needle which is attached to the coil are proportional to the current flowing. In the ammeter there is a shunt which carries the major portion of the current. In the voltmeter there is a high-resistance series coil which reduces the current through the movable coil, and the current is proportional to the voltage across the terminals of the instrument.

With reasonable care there is little danger of injuring the voltmeter, provided one uses an instrument of sufficient range. Experience shows that most of the accidents occur in the use of the ammeter. This is due to the fact that there must always be in the circuit sufficient resistance to regulate the current flowing through the instrument. For example, if a 30-ampere ammeter is connected directly across a 6-volt

* If a 6-volt storage battery is used, the coils A and B which were used in Experiment 37 will serve very well.

storage battery, the instrument is burned out before it can be disconnected. This is because the battery has almost negligible internal resistance and because the resistance of the instrument is also very small. Therefore the rush of current is excessive.

In this experiment we shall learn how to place the ammeter to measure the current; also, how to place the voltmeter to measure the voltage in a series circuit and in a parallel circuit. From these we can calculate the resistance of the resistors in series and in parallel. It will be well to have your connections approved by your instructor before you connect with the source of electricity.

Directions. I. _Measurement of current. Series._ Join the two resistors in series and connect with the 110-volt d-c. service or other supply of steady current. Place the

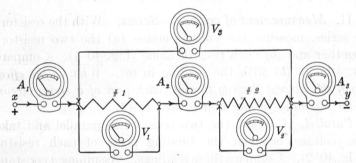

Fig. 40–1. A series circuit. Current is measured by A_1, A_2, and A_3; voltage by V_1, V_2, and V_3.

ammeter (_a_) between resistor #1 and the power supply (Fig. 40–1), (_b_) between resistor #1 and resistor #2, (_c_) between resistor #2 and the power. Record the average reading of the ammeter in each position. _What do you conclude about the current in a series circuit? Where should the ammeter be placed in a series circuit?_

Parallel. Join the two resistors in parallel and measure the current with the ammeter (_a_) in the line between the coils and the power supply (Fig. 40–2), (b) in the circuit of resistor #1 alone, and (c) in the circuit of resistor #2 alone. Compare the sum of currents in (b) and (c) with the current in (a). *Where must the ammeter be placed to measure the total current in a branched circuit? Where to measure the current in each branch?*

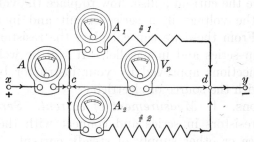

Fig. 40–2.   Two resistors in parallel.

II. *Measurement of voltage. Series.* With the resistors in series, measure the voltage across (a) the two resistors together and (b) each resistor alone (Fig. 40–1). Compare the sum in (b) with the reading in (a). *What is the effect upon the current flowing through each part of a series circuit if the resistance of any unit is decreased?*

Parallel. Connect the two resistors in parallel and take the voltage between the binding posts of each resistor (Fig. 40–2). Compare these readings. Assuming a constant voltage service, *what do you find to be the effect upon the voltage across the group if the resistance of one resistor is decreased? Upon the current flowing in that coil? Upon the current in the other coil? In the line?*

III. *Computation of resistance.* From the readings in Parts I and II, compute, using Ohm's Law $\left(R = \dfrac{E}{I}\right)$, (a) the resistance of each resistor, (b) the combined resistance of the two resistors in series, and (c) the joint resistance of the two resistors in parallel. Compare this latter result with that obtained by computing the joint resistance from the separate resistances $\left(\dfrac{1}{R} = \dfrac{1}{R_1} + \dfrac{1}{R_2}\right)$. In recording the data of this experiment, make careful diagrams to show the connections.

EXPERIMENT 41

MEASUREMENT OF RESISTANCE BY WHEATSTONE BRIDGE

How can an unknown resistance be compared with a known resistance by means of a Wheatstone bridge?

Wheatstone bridge (meter-wire form)	D'Arsonval galvanometer
	Resistance box, dial form
Dry cells	Connecting wires
Key	Unknown resistor to be measured

Introduction. The Wheatstone bridge consists essentially of a loop of four resistors, indicated in figure 41–1 as R, X,

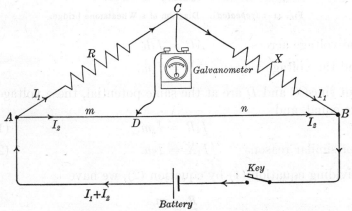

Fig. 41–1. Diagram of a Wheatstone bridge.

m, and n. When the key is closed, the current from the cells flows into the loop at A and there divides so that part (I_1)

goes through AC and part (I_2) through AD. A sensitive galvanometer is connected between C and D. Then the resistances R, X, m, and n are so adjusted that no current flows through the galvanometer, which means that all of I_1 has to go on through CB and all of I_2 through DB. This also means that C and D are "equipotential" points. When this adjustment has been made,

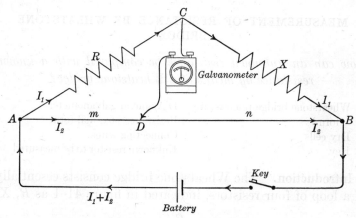

Fig. 41–1 (*repeated*).   Diagram of a Wheatstone bridge.

the voltage across $\qquad AC = I_1R$

and the voltage across $\quad AD = I_2m$.

But since C and D are at the same potential, these voltages are equal, and

$$I_1R = I_2m. \tag{1}$$

For similar reasons $\qquad I_1X = I_2n. \tag{2}$

Dividing equation (1) by equation (2), we have

$$\frac{R}{X} = \frac{m}{n}.$$

From this fundamental equation of the Wheatstone bridge, if we know R, m, and n, we can compute X.

In the form of this apparatus shown in figure 41–2, the resistance ADB consists of a wire one meter long and of uniform cross section. Since the resistances m and n in

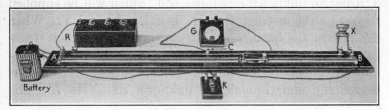

Fig. 41–2.   Measuring resistance with a Wheatstone bridge.

figure 41–3 are then directly proportional to the distances AD and DB, the equation becomes

$$\frac{R}{X} = \frac{\text{distance } AD}{\text{distance } DB}$$

where R is a known resistance, such as a resistance box, and the distances AD and DB are read off on a meter stick. It will be helpful to remember that

$$\frac{\text{Left resistance}}{\text{Right resistance}} = \frac{\text{left distance}}{\text{right distance}}.$$

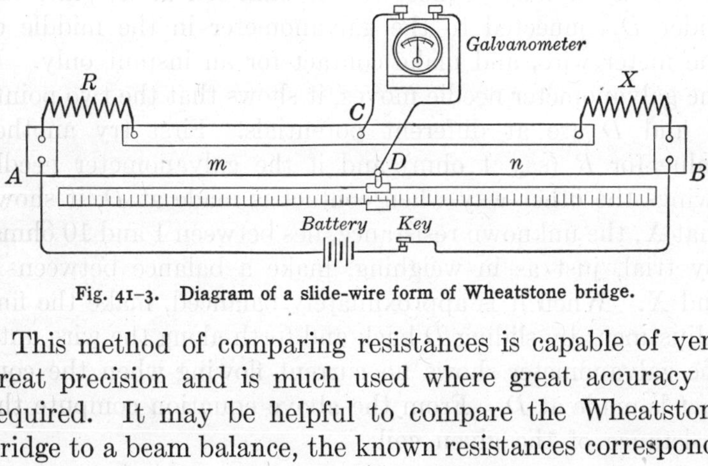

Fig. 41–3.   Diagram of a slide-wire form of Wheatstone bridge.

This method of comparing resistances is capable of very great precision and is much used where great accuracy is required. It may be helpful to compare the Wheatstone bridge to a beam balance, the known resistances corresponding to the set of known weights. When m equals n, we have an equal-arm balance and R equals X.

Directions. Connect the apparatus, as shown in figure 41–3, using an unknown resistance coil (which will be supplied to you by the instructor) in the position marked X. When the key in the battery circuit is closed, the current comes to A. Here it divides, part going through the known resistance R, along the bar of the bridge (whose resistance is negligible), and through the unknown coil X to B. The

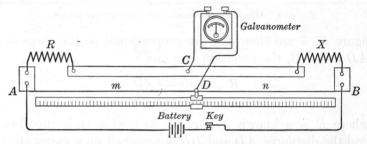

Fig. 41–3 (*repeated*). Diagram of a slide-wire form of Wheatstone bridge.

other part goes by way of the high-resistance wire ADB to B. If the known resistance is made in the form of a resistance box, we may connect the 10-ohm coil at R, place the slider D connected to the galvanometer in the middle of the meter wire, and make contact for an instant only. If the galvanometer needle moves, it shows that the two points C and D are at different potentials. First try another value for R (say 1 ohm) and if the galvanometer needle swings the other way when contact is made at D, it shows that X, the unknown resistance, lies between 1 and 10 ohms. By trial, just as in weighing, make a balance between R and X. When it is approximately balanced, make the fine adjustment by sliding D back and forth along the wire until the galvanometer shows no current flowing when the contact is made at D. From the above equation compute the resistance of the given coil.

Repeat the experiment twice, using slightly different values for R, the known resistance. Find the average, or mean, value of these three results. Check your result with the accepted value, which will be furnished by the instructor.

*   *   *   *

Effect of temperature on resistance. The resistance of pure metals increases with the temperature. The temperature coefficient of resistance of a metal is the increase in resistance of a one-ohm coil of that metal when heated 1° C. By means of a Wheatstone bridge, we may measure the resistance of a coil of copper wire when cold and again when hot. If we know the temperature in each case, we can easily compute the coefficient. It will be convenient to use a bifilar coil of bare copper wire wound on a fiber tube provided with heavy connecting wires. This coil may be placed in a tube filled with oil. Then the tube may be surrounded by ice water and steam in turn.

This effect of temperature on the resistance of copper may be expressed in the form of an equation:

$$R_t = R_o (1 + kt)$$

where R_t = resistance at $t°$ C., R_0 = resistance at 0° C., and t = temperature of wire in degrees centigrade.

From the experimental data in this experiment, compute the temperature coefficient, k. Compare this value with that usually given in ENGINEER'S HANDBOOKS, namely 0.00426.

ELECTRICITY (*continued*)

BLOCK VI. EFFECTS OF ELECTRIC CURRENT

Suggestive Questions

1. *Is the electric supply in your home direct or alternating current?*
2. *How could you answer the first question experimentally?*
3. *How is the 6-volt battery current of an automobile raised to several thousand volts for ignition purposes?*
4. *What is the purpose of the condenser used in the ignition system of an automobile?*
5. *How does the charging current generated in an automobile depend upon the speed?*
6. *Why can't the electrolysis of water be carried on satisfactorily with alternating current?*
7. *Could you use a transformer on a direct-current system?*
8. *Why is the iron box containing a transformer usually filled with oil?*
9. *How would you make a permanent magnet with a bar of hardened steel, a coil of insulated copper wire, and a supply of alternating current?*
10. *Is it cheaper to operate a flatiron on alternating current or direct current?*
11. *Will a "telechron clock" operate on a direct-current line?*
12. *What advantage is there in using an electromagnet instead of a permanent magnet in the field of a generator?*
13. *What is the purpose of an ammeter on the dashboard of an automobile?*
14. *Why does the compass needle sometimes deviate from the true north and south line?*

166

EXPERIMENT 42

MAGNETIC EFFECT OF A CURRENT

I. *What is the direction of the magnetic lines of force about a wire carrying an electric current?*

II. *How is the distribution of magnetic flux passing through a coil changed by inserting a soft-iron core?*

Dry cell	Compass (2.5-cm. needle)
Switch or key	Soft-iron rod or core
Connecting wires	U-shaped iron core

Introduction. One of the difficulties about electric currents and one of their fascinating characteristics is that they are invisible. We study electricity largely through its effects, and of all these effects the magnetic effect is doubtless the most useful. As long ago as 1819 a Danish physicist named Oersted discovered that an electric current flowing along a wire near a compass deflected the needle from its usual north and south position. This led to a study of the magnetic field around a straight wire carrying a current, around a loop or coil of wire, and finally around a coil of wire with an iron core. This iron core surrounded by a coil of insulated wire, called an **electromagnet,** is an essential part of the electric bell, telegraph, and telephone, as well as of the electric generator and motor.

In this experiment we shall study the magnetic field about a straight wire and about a coil carrying a current. Then we shall study the practical application of these principles in the electromagnet. We shall assume that the *N*-pole of the magnetic needle points in the direction of the magnetic lines of force and that the direction in which the electricity flows through a dry cell is from zinc to carbon inside the cell and *from carbon to zinc in the external circuit.*

Directions. I. *Magnetic field about a wire carrying current.* (*a*) Connect a dry cell to a switch and then lead the

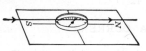

Fig. 42-1. Current flowing over a compass.

current from south to north over a compass, as shown in figure 42-1. Close the circuit by means of the switch and *record the deflection.*

(*b*) Reverse the current, causing it to flow from north to south over the compass. *Record the deflection.*

Compare these results with what might be expected from the so-called **thumb rule**:

If one grasps the wire with the right hand so that the thumb points in the direction of the current, the fingers will point in the direction of the magnetic field.

(*c*) Put the wire under the compass and, without changing the direction of the current, *note the direction of the deflection.*

(*d*) Pass the current from the cell over the compass from south to north, holding the wire close to the face of the compass. Make the return wire pass under the compass so that a loop is made around the compass. *Is the deflection greater or less than in (a)? Why?*

II. *Magnetic field about a coil carrying current.* (*a*) Loop the wire used in I (*d*) several times around the compass in such a way that the plane of the coil is north and south. *What change in the deflection is produced by increasing the number of turns in the coil?*

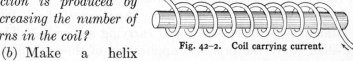

Fig. 42-2. Coil carrying current.

(*b*) Make a helix (Fig. 42-2) by wrapping the wire, say fifty times, around a lead pencil. Connect this to the switch as in I. See whether or not such a helix carrying a current acts as a magnet with one end attracting the north pole of the compass and the other repelling it. Reverse the current through the helix by means of a reversing switch. Record the effect that is produced upon the poles. *Record the results in a diagram.*

Compare these results with what might be expected from the **thumb rule for a coil**:

Grasp the coil with the right hand so that the fingers point in the direction of the current in the coil, and the thumb will point to the north pole of the coil.

III. **Electromagnet.** (*a*) Make an electromagnet by putting a large iron nail or bolt inside the helix. *Does this iron core make the poles stronger or weaker than before? How do you know?*

(*b*) Wind the two sides of the U-shaped piece of iron with a wire carrying a current, in such a way that one end which has already been marked will be a *N*-pole and the other a *S*-pole.

Test the polarity of this horseshoe with a compass.

In recording the results of these experiments, make very simple but clear diagrams, showing the polarity and the direction of the current in each case.

*   *   *   *

The electric bell. Remove the metal cap covering the *electromagnet* and identify the *armature,* the *spring,* and the *contact point.* Trace the electric circuit through the bell from one binding post to the other. Does the iron base serve as part of the circuit? Note the change in the circuit as the armature vibrates back and forth. Draw a simple but clear diagram of the bell and label its parts.

Connect two push buttons with the bell and a dry cell so that the bell will ring when either button is pushed. Make a diagram to show the connections.

EXPERIMENT 43

ELECTROLYSIS OF WATER

How may an ammeter be calibrated by the volume of hydrogen generated in a certain length of time?

Hydrogen coulometer
Dilute sulfuric acid (1 : 10)
Ammeter (0 − 3)

Adjustable resistance
Storage battery or supply of steady current

Watch or clock with second hand

Introduction. By international agreement the practical unit of quantity of electricity is the **coulomb**. This unit is defined as that quantity of electricity which deposits 0.001118 gram of silver. It has also been agreed that the unit rate at which electricity flows along a conductor shall be the **ampere,** or one coulomb per second. Usually we are more interested in the rate of flow (amperes) than in the quantity of electricity (coulombs). Therefore we frequently use ammeters (or ampere meters) but only occasionally coulometers. We may use the latter to calibrate an ammeter.

The coulometer depends on the chemical effect of an electric current. When an electric current passes through a water solution of a salt, base, or acid, the latter is decomposed. The products of decomposition usually appear at the electrodes, which lead the current into and out of the solution. If the solution is an acid, such as sulfuric acid, hydrogen gas appears at the **cathode** (the terminal by which the current leaves the solution). If the solution contains a metallic salt, such as silver nitrate or copper sulfate, the metal is often deposited on the cathode. Now the quantity of metal deposited or of gas generated depends directly upon the quantity of electricity passing through the solution. The weight of hydrogen generated under certain specific conditions has been very carefully determined. It has been found to be 0.0378 gram per ampere-hour.

170

The object of this experiment is to calibrate an ammeter, that is, find the error in an ammeter by means of a hydrogen coulometer.

Directions. The hydrogen coulometer consists of two vertical glass tubes, one inside the other. The outer one

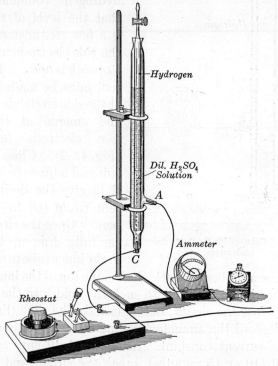

Fig. 43–1. **Measuring the hydrogen evolved by an electric current in one second.**

is closed at the bottom. In this end is sealed a platinum electrode (the cathode). The inner tube is open at the bottom and graduated in cubic centimeters from the stopcock down. The open end of this tube fits over the lower platinum electrode so as to collect the hydrogen gas. The anode is sealed into the side wall of the outer tube as shown in figure 43–1.

Connect the ammeter A which is to be calibrated with an adjustable rheostat R in series with the coulometer and

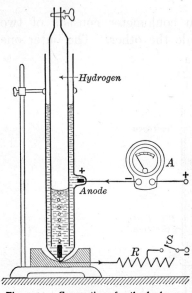

some supply of steady current, such as a storage battery (Fig. 43–2). Fill the hydrogen coulometer so that the level of the acid is a few centimeters above the side electrode when the stopcock is open. The current must be made to enter at the side electrode (anode) and emerge at the bottom electrode (cathode) (Fig. 43–2). Close the circuit and adjust the rheostat R to give the desired current (from 0.5 to 1.0 ampere). Open the circuit and carefully draw up the acid in the inner tube to the stop-

Fig. 43–2. Connections for the hydrogen coulometer.

cock. Use a rubber tube attached to the top of the inner tube. Some care is required not to suck the acid into the mouth.

Again close the circuit, noting exactly the time (hr., min., sec.). Record the ammeter reading every two minutes and keep the current constant. After about 40 cm.³ of gas is collected (10 or 15 minutes), break the circuit and at once record the exact time. Raise the inner tube until the level of the acid is the same in both tubes. Record the reading on the inner tube. Make a record of the temperature of the room and barometric pressure.

Compute the volume of hydrogen generated per hour.

From Table XI in the Appendix, which gives the Density of Hydrogen at varying temperatures and pressures, *compute the weight of the hydrogen collected per hour.*

Assuming that 0.0378 gram of hydrogen is generated per ampere-hour, *compute the average current.*

Compare this value of the current with the average reading of the ammeter.

It will be convenient to record the data and results in tabular form somewhat as follows:

Data

Barometer reading . . . .   cm.
Temperature of room . . . .   ° C.
Volume of hydrogen . . . .   cm.³
Average reading of ammeter . . . .   ampere
Time of starting . . . . . .   hr.   min.   sec.
Time of stopping . . . . . .   hr.   min.   sec.

Results

Time of run . . . . min., or   hr.
Weight of hydrogen (from Table) . . . .   g.
Assuming the electrochemical equivalent of hydrogen to be 0.0378 g. per ampere-hour,
Calculated value of current . . . .   ampere
Average reading of ammeter . . . .   ampere
Error in ammeter . . . .   ampere

NOTE. This experiment may be done as a CLASS EXPERIMENT using the familiar Hoffman apparatus for the electrolysis of water.

ALTERNATIVE EXPERIMENT 43A

COPPER COULOMETER

How may an ammeter be calibrated by the weight of copper deposited in a certain length of time?

Copper coulometer
Copper sulfate ($CuSO_4$) solution
   with a little acid and alcohol
Ammeter (0 − 3)

Watch or clock with second hand
Beam or Jolly balance with weights
Storage battery or some other supply of steady current

Adjustable rheostat

Directions. The copper coulometer consists of a glass jar with two copper anode plates A, A and one cathode, or gain, plate C placed between them (Fig. 43–3). About 50 square centimeters of cathode surface is allowed for each ampere of current. The liquid is a solution of copper sulfate ($CuSO_4$) slightly acidulated with sulfuric acid (H_2SO_4) and containing a little alcohol.* The gain plate (cathode) is first made perfectly clean by rubbing with fine emery until bright and then wiping with a clean dry cloth. After it is cleaned, the part which is to be immersed must not be touched by the fingers.

Weigh this clean cathode as accurately as you can and set it aside.

Connect the ammeter which is to be calibrated with an adjustable rheostat in series with the coulometer and some supply of steady current, such as a storage battery. The current must be made to enter at the outside plates (anodes) and emerge at the middle, or gain, plate (cathode) (Fig. 43–4). Close the circuit and adjust the rheostat to give the desired current (from 1 to 2 amperes). Close the circuit, noting the time (hr., min., sec.) exactly. Record the ammeter reading every two minutes and keep the current

* Add 200 g. crystallized copper sulfate to 1000 cm.³ water and when it is all in solution, filter and add 50 g. sulfuric acid and 50 g. alcohol (ethyl).

constant. After 30 or 40 minutes, break the circuit and at once remove the gain plate. Note the deposit of copper. Rinse off in clean water and then in alcohol and dry quickly. Reweigh and determine the gain as precisely as possible.

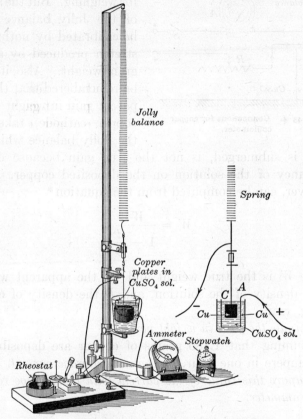

Fig. 43–3. Copper coulometer for calibrating an ammeter

If the Jolly balance is used, the gain plate is suspended from the spring, midway between the anode plates, and entirely submerged in the copper sulfate solution. Only a single fine wire should extend through the surface of the liquid.

The electrical connection with the gain plate is made by a clamp on the suspension wire. In this way the gain

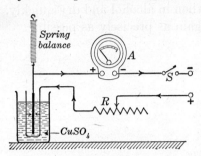

plate does not have to be removed from the solution for weighing. But the spring of the Jolly balance must be calibrated by noting the stretch produced by a one-gram weight. Also, it must be remembered that the apparent gain in weight of the copper cathode, taken on the Jolly balance while the

Fig. 43-4. Connections for copper coulometer.

plate is submerged, is not the true gain because of the buoyancy of the solution on the deposited copper. This, however, can be computed from the equation *

$$W = \frac{W'}{1 - \dfrac{d}{D}}$$

where W is the true weight and W' the apparent weight, d the density of the solution, and D the density of copper (8.9 g./cm.^{3}).

Compute the gain in weight per hour.

Assuming that 1.186 grams of copper are deposited by one ampere in one hour, *compute the average current.*

Compare this value of the current with the average reading of the ammeter.

* From Archimedes' principle we know

$$W' = W - \frac{W}{D} d.$$

EXPERIMENT 44

CHARGE AND DISCHARGE OF A STORAGE BATTERY

How do the voltage and the density of the electrolyte change during the process of charge and discharge?

Storage battery (3 cells)
Voltmeter (0 — 15)
Ammeter (0 — 30)
Hydrometer, syringe form

Rectifier, such as copper-oxide, for a-c. circuit
Bank of lamps, to control discharging current or charging current on d-c. circuit

Introduction. The extensive use of the storage battery on automobiles for starting, lighting, and ignition purposes has made some knowledge of its proper use an everyday necessity. What you see on the outside is a black box with lead strips at the top. In this box are three cells if it is a 6-volt battery. Each cell is contained in a jar of hard rubber or of some other insulating material. The positive plates, which are brown in color, are coated with lead dioxide (PbO_2). The negative plates, which are gray, are made of spongy lead (Pb). These plates are sandwiched together with one more negative plate than positive. In these portable batteries the plates are made very thin and are set very close together with insulating separators (usually of wood) between. The electrolyte consists of sulfuric acid and distilled water (about 1 part acid to 3 parts water by volume).

To charge a storage battery, wires from a d-c. generator or d-c. line are connected with the lead terminals and a direct current of electricity is passed through it for several hours. During this process oxygen is generated at the positive plates, forming lead dioxide, and hydrogen at the negative plates. The electricity is not stored in the battery but produces a chemical change which may be represented as follows:

Discharge ⟶

POSITIVE   ELECTROLYTE   NEGATIVE

$$PbO_2 \; + \; 2\,H_2SO_4 \; + \; Pb \; = \; 2\,PbSO_4 \; + \; 2\,H_2O$$

Lead dioxide   *Sulfuric acid*   *Lead*   *Lead sulfate*   *Water*

⟵ Charge.

When the storage battery is being used, that is, when it dis-
charges, the chemical action takes place in the reverse
direction and the lead dioxide is slowly used up. Inci-
dentally, the solution becomes more dilute with the forma-
tion of water, as shown in the chemical equation. Thus we
see that we can learn very much about the condition of a
storage battery by determining the density of its electrolyte.

Directions. *Charging.* Connect the storage battery to
some source of direct current, such as a dry-plate rectifier or a
110-volt d-c. line, with a lamp bank to control the current.
Be sure to connect the positive terminal (marked + or red)
of the battery to the positive wire of the line. Insert an
ammeter in series with the battery and adjust the charging
current to about 3 amperes. Connect a voltmeter so as to
read the voltage across the terminals of the battery. At
regular intervals of 5 minutes each, record the voltage,
current, and time. With each set of readings the charging
circuit should be open long enough to read the voltage of the
battery. Also measure the density of the electrolyte by
means of a hydrometer. Continue the process of charging
until the density of the acid solution becomes constant.

Discharging. Allow the battery to discharge through a
bank of lamps or a rheostat which takes about 3 amperes.
Again read the ammeter, voltmeter, and hydrometer at
regular intervals of 5 minutes each until the density of the
electrolyte becomes 1.150.

Results. In a series of curves, show the change of *voltage*
(vertically) and change in *density* of the electrolyte (vertically) with *time* on charge (horizontally). In the same way
curves may be plotted to show these changes with discharge.

Assuming that we discharge the battery to the same condition as when we started charging, we may compute its efficiency; that is, the ratio of the watt-hours got out to the watt-hours put in. Thus,

$$\text{Efficiency} = \frac{\text{watt-hours output}}{\text{watt-hours input to recharge}}$$

$$= \frac{\text{amp.-hours output} \times \text{av. discharge voltage}}{\text{amp.-hours input} \times \text{av. charging voltage}}$$

* * * *

Efficiency of the rectifier. In this experiment we shall use the dry-plate type of rectifier. The essential parts are shown in figure 44–1. It consists of a step-down transformer and a copper-oxide rectifier. The action depends on the fact that when plates of copper and cuprous oxide are firmly pressed together, an electric current will easily pass from the oxide to the copper but not from the copper to the oxide. Just why this action occurs is not yet settled. The connections are shown in figure 44–2.

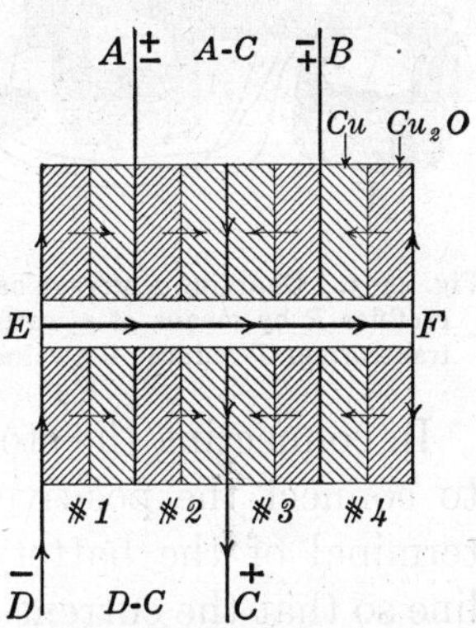

Fig. 44–1. Diagram of the copper-oxide rectifier.

To measure the efficiency of the rectifier, we must use a wattmeter to get the a-c. input and can use a voltmeter and ammeter to get the d-c. output.

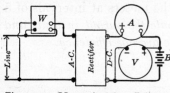

Fig. 44–2. Measuring the efficiency of a rectifier.

Directions. Connect the wattmeter (Fig. 44–3) so as to measure the a-c. input. The instrument consists of two sets of coils. One is stationary and carries the full current. The other is movable, consists of the potential coils, and carries only a small current proportional to the voltage. The current terminals are large and metallic. The potential terminals are smaller and capped with some insulating material. Therefore connect the wattmeter with the current terminals inserted *in* the line, just as you would an ammeter, and with the potential terminals *across* the line, just as you would a voltmeter.

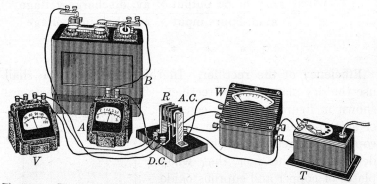

Fig. 44–3. Charging a storage battery *B* and measuring the efficiency of the dry-plate rectifier *R* by means of a wattmeter *W* and a voltmeter *V* and ammeter *A*. The transformer *T* reduces the voltage from 115 to 8 volts.

In connecting the storage battery to the rectifier, be sure to connect the positive terminal (red) to the positive (+) terminal of the battery. Insert the d-c. ammeter in the line so that the current enters the ammeter at the + binding post. The voltmeter is connected across the terminals of the battery. When everything is connected and before you close the switch, have the instructor approve your apparatus.

Turn on the current and read the meters at intervals of 5 minutes for half an hour. *Compute the output in watts and the efficiency in per cent. Find the average efficiency.*

THE ELECTRICAL EQUIVALENT OF HEAT. JOULE'S LAW

I. *How many watt-seconds (joules) are required to produce one calorie?*

II. *What is the combined efficiency of an electric stove and a kettle?*

Doubled-walled calorimeter	Saucepan (4-qt.)
Heating coil and stirrer	2 Thermometers, 0.1° and 1.0° C.
Control rheostat	Electric stove (hot-plate)
Voltmeter (0 — 15; 0 — 150)	Connecting wires
Ammeter (0 — 3; 0 — 30)	Clock (telechron)

Introduction. Electric heating appliances are very convenient but more expensive to operate than gas appliances. In spite of this handicap, electric flatirons, toasters, percolators, chafing dishes, and radiators are now common in the household, and electric soldering irons, glue cookers, melting pots, automobile-tire vulcanizers, and electric ovens are much used industrially. The principle is the same in all these devices. The electrical energy is transformed into heat by resistance, just as mechanical energy may be transformed into heat by friction. The heating element of the electric stove consists of a high-resistance ribbon or wire which is supported on or embedded in some insulating material.

The user of such an appliance wants to know the cost of the heat obtained from the electrical energy and also the efficiency of the appliance. To determine these we shall need to do two experiments:

(1) Measure the quantity of heat derived from a measured quantity of electrical energy when *all* the heat is conserved.

(2) Measure the electrical energy required to heat a pan of water on an electric stove in which *only part* of the heat is utilized.

Directions. In the first experiment we shall use a double-walled calorimeter.* The temperature range is so chosen that the initial temperature is as much below that of the room as the final temperature is above it. The heat generated is computed from the following equation:

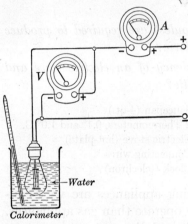

A

V

—Water

Calorimeter

Fig. 45-1. Connections for measuring the electrical equivalent of heat by means of a lamp bulb.

$$H = (W + 0.1\ C)\ (t_2 - t_1)$$

in which H is expressed in calories. W is the weight of the water, and C the weight of the inner cup of the calorimeter in grams. The final and initial temperatures are t_2 and t_1.

To determine the quantity of electrical energy (watt-seconds or joules) consumed, we connect the electric circuit so as to measure the current in the heater and the voltage across the heater (Fig. 45-2). Before switching on the current, it will be well to let the instructor inspect your connections. *Do not turn on the current unless the coil is immersed in water! Why not?*

Note precisely the times at which the current is started and stopped, and compute the time of the run in seconds. Read the voltmeter and ammeter every half-minute so as to obtain the average value for the voltage and current. The energy consumed will then be computed from the following equation:

Joules = volts × amperes × seconds.

* In case the electric calorimeter is not available, we may substitute an incandescent lamp bulb immersed in water in a beaker (Fig. 45-1). If the voltmeter and ammeter of proper range are not at hand, use the wattage marked on the lamp bulb.

Result. Assuming that no heat is lost in the experiment, *we may compute the number of joules required to produce one calorie.*

*   *   *   *

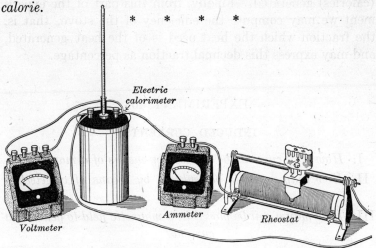

Fig. 45-2.   Measuring the heating effect of an electric current.

Efficiency of an electric stove. We repeat the first experiment, using a hot plate and dish or pan of water instead of the calorimeter. Be sure the meters are connected with the proper range to use about 6 amperes at 110 volts. The heat (calories) developed is measured as before

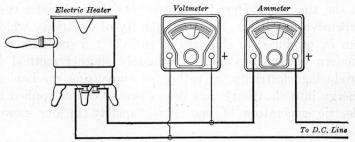

Fig. 45-3.   How much electric power does the heater take?

by the rise in temperature of a known weight of water and dish. The electrical energy is determined as before by computing the number of joules consumed (Fig. 45-3). Then, using the electrical equivalent of heat (which has been determined in the first experiment), we may compute the heat (calories) generated. Finally, from this part of the experiment we may compute the efficiency of the stove, that is, the fraction which the heat used is of the heat generated, and may express this decimal fraction as percentage.

EXPERIMENT 46

INDUCED CURRENTS

I. *How may currents be induced by means of a magnet?*

II. *How may currents be induced by means of an electromagnet?*

III. *How may a coil be moved in a magnetic field to generate a current?*

D'Arsonval galvanometer	Bar magnet
2 Dry cells	Soft-iron core
2 Coils of about 600 turns of	Reversing switch
No. 28 copper wire	U-shaped steel magnet

Introduction. The dry cell produces an electric current by means of the chemical action of the sal ammoniac paste in the zinc can. Here the zinc acts as the fuel and a very expensive fuel it is. But the quantity of electricity which can be produced in this way is entirely too small for our modern power purposes. Fortunately another method of producing electricity, or rather, of converting mechanical energy into electricity, has been discovered and applied in electric generators of enormous capacity in our power stations.

In this experiment we shall study the fundamental principles of induced currents produced by a permanent magnet, by an electromagnet, and by a coil moving in a magnetic field.

Directions. I. *Induction by a magnet.* To see which way the needle of the d'Arsonval galvanometer moves when the current enters at the right-hand binding post, we short-circuit the instrument with a stout copper wire and connect it with a dry cell so that the current from the + pole enters at the right-hand terminal of the galvanometer. Place a piece of paper near the instrument and record the direction of the deflection with an arrow when the right terminal is made positive (+). Connect the galvanometer (now without any shunt) with a coil of many turns (about 800 turns of No. 28 copper wire).

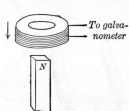

Fig. 46–1. Current induced in coil.

(*a*) Now quickly move the coil downward over the *N*-pole of the bar magnet and record the direction and amount of the deflection. From this deflection determine the direction of the current induced in the coil. While this current was flowing in the coil, it made the coil a temporary magnet. *What was the polarity of the side of the coil approaching the N-pole of the magnet?*

NOTE. In recording the results of these experiments, it will be helpful to use simple diagrams (Fig. 46–1). With arrows and labels, show the direction of the motion and of the current, as well as the poles.

(*b*) Quickly remove the coil from the magnet and record the direction and amount of the deflection. Compare the direction and amount of the current thus induced with that in part (*a*). *What is the polarity of the end of the coil that last leaves the magnet's N-pole?*

(*c*) Repeat (*a*) and (*b*) thrusting the *N*-pole of the magnet into the coil (Fig. 46–2). In each case determine the direction of the current induced in the coil. *Is the direction of the induced current such as to oppose or to assist the motion of the coil?* (Lenz's Law)

II. *Induction by an electromagnet.* Insert an iron rod in one coil (*secondary*) which is connected with the galva-

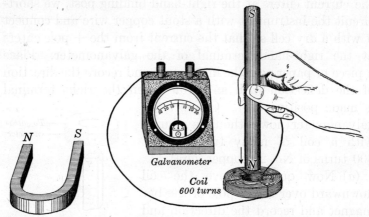

Fig. 46–2.   A current induced by moving a magnet in and out of a coil.

nometer.   Connect through a switch one or two dry cells to a similar coil (*primary*) which is placed on the iron rod beside the secondary coil (Fig. 46–3).

(*a*) Now close the circuit with the switch and record the deflection of the galvanometer.   From this determine the

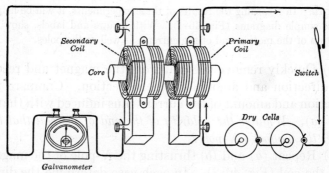

Fig. 46–3.   A current induced in the secondary coil.

direction of the current induced in the secondary coil.   *Was the current induced in the **secondary** coil in the same direction* *as the current in the **primary** coil? Explain how this might be expected from the experiment in Part I.*

(b) Break the circuit at the switch and note direction and amount of the deflection. Compare this with that induced when the circuit is closed.

Is the induced current in the same direction as that which is flowing in the primary coil or in the opposite direction? Note that the current is induced by the *changes* in the magnetism of the electromagnet. *Is the direction of the induced current such as to oppose or assist the changes in the magnetism of the iron core?*

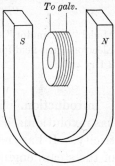

Fig. 46–4. Effect of turning the coil.

III. *A current generated by moving a coil in a magnetic field.* Hold a coil which is connected with the galvanometer between the poles of a U-magnet in such a way that the plane of the coil is at right angles to the line joining the poles (Fig. 46–4). Quickly move the coil a quarter turn about a vertical axis so that the plane of the coil is parallel to the magnetic field. Observe the direction of the induced current. After the galvanometer has come back to zero, rotate the coil another quarter turn and note the direction of the induced current. In a similar manner continue to rotate the coil one quarter turn at a time. *In what position is the coil when the induced current is reversed?*

EXPERIMENT 47

ELECTRIC GENERATOR AND MOTOR

I. *What are the fundamental principles upon which the electric generator operates?*

II. *What are the fundamental principles which control the operation of an electric motor?*

Model " genamotor " (Cambosco)   Galvanometer
Electromagnet field for genamotor   Small variable rheostat (10 ohms)
2 Dry cells   Compass
Switch

Introduction. The development of the electric generator has revolutionized modern industry by furnishing cheap electricity. It has enabled us to transform the enormous energy of the steam engine and water wheel into electricity. After the discovery of induced currents by Faraday and Henry, it took about 40 years to develop a practical generator.

Today we use the electric motor for so many purposes in the home, on the streets, and in the shop, that we are likely to forget that it is the result of a vast amount of experimental study. Nevertheless we shall learn that the essential parts of a generator or motor are few and that their operation is simple to understand.

First let us remember that a **generator** is a *reversible* machine. When it is supplied with electricity and used to drive some other machine like a street car or sewing machine, we call it a **motor**. The most important parts of this machine, sometimes called a dynamo, are (1) the *field*, which furnishes the magnetic flux; (2) the *armature*, usually the rotating element and the one in which a current is generated or which, if supplied with current, produces rotation; (3) the *commutator* (in a-c. machines the slip rings), at which the current is collected or through which the current is sent into the armature; (4) the *brushes*, which slide on the commutator (or rings) and provide a method of taking off the current or putting it into the armature.

Directions. I. *Magneto.* Put the armature with the slip rings in position and bring the permanent U-magnet up close to the armature (Fig. 47–1). Adjust the brushes so that they rest on the slip rings and then connect the brushes to the galvanometer.

Fig. 47–1.   A rotating armature *A* between the poles *NS* of a permanent magnet *M* generates an alternating current in the galvanometer *G*.

(*a*) Slowly rotate the armature and note carefully the deflections of the galvanometer. *Is the induced current alternating or unidirectional? If alternating, in what position is the armature when the current reverses its direction?*

(*b*) Rotate the armature at different speeds. *What is the effect on the induced current of increasing the speed?*

II. *Direct-current generator.* Change the brushes from the slip-ring end of the armature to the other end, which has a commutator. Carefully adjust the brushes. Set the permanent U-magnet close to the armature.

(*a*) Rotate the armature in one direction and note the direction of the deflection. Rotate in the opposite direction and note the direction of the deflection. *Explain.*

(*b*) Rotate the armature at different speeds. *How does increasing the speed affect the induced current?*

(c) Move the U-magnet farther away from the armature and *note the effect on the induced current. What two factors have you found that affect the induced current and therefore the electromotive force produced by a generator?*

Fig. 47–2. A shunt motor with armature and field separately excited by dry cells, B_a and B_f.

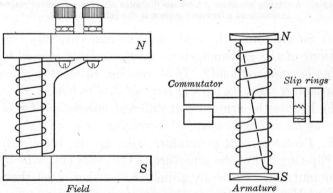

Fig. 47–2. Diagrams of windings on the field and armature.

III. *Direct-current motor.* Remove the galvanometer and connect a cell in series with the armature and a switch. Set the brushes so that the polarity of the armature core changes at the proper place to produce continuous rotation.

Test with a small compass the polarity of the core for a complete revolution of the armature.

(a) Find what effect is produced on the speed of the motor by the gradual weakening of the field when the U-magnet is moved away from the armature.

(b) Find the effect on the speed of the motor of reducing the armature current. This may be done by introducing resistance or using one dry cell instead of two.

(c) *How would you reverse the direction of rotation of a motor?* Try the effect of reversing the armature current. Try the effect of reversing the magnetic field by turning the magnet end for end. Try the effect of reversing *both* the armature current and the field.

* * * *

Series- and shunt-wound motor. Remove the permanent magnet and connect an electromagnet with a dry cell B_f. Connect the armature with another dry cell B_a as shown

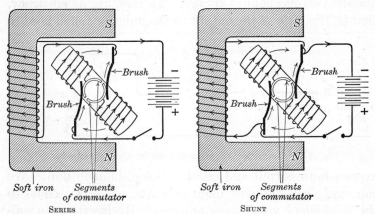

Fig. 47–3. Connections for a *series* and for a *shunt* motor.

in figure 47–2. Reverse the current in the field coil, then in the armature, and finally in both. *Explain the effect.*

Connect two dry cells with the motor, having the electromagnet in *series* with the armature (Fig. 47–3). Reverse the current from the battery. *Explain the effect, if any, on the direction of rotation.*

Connect the electromagnetic field in *parallel* with the armature (Fig. 47–3). Reverse the current from the battery. *Explain the effect, if any, on the direction of rotation.*

EXPERIMENT 48

EFFICIENCY OF AN ELECTRIC MOTOR *

What is the ratio of the mechanical output of an electric motor to the electrical input?

Shunt motor (0.25 horsepower)	Two spring balances (20 lbs.)
110-volt direct-current line or	and support
storage battery	Cord or strap for brake
Ammeter (0 — 30)	Speed counter
Voltmeter (0 — 150)	Watch

Introduction. An electric motor receives electrical energy and delivers mechanical energy. To compute its efficiency, that is, the ratio of the output to the input, we shall need to

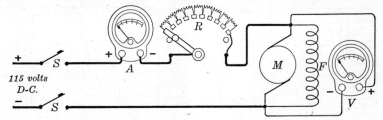

Fig. 48–1. Connections for measuring the *input* to a shunt motor.

express both output and input in some common unit. We can easily calculate the **input** in watts, which are equal to the product of volts times amperes. By inserting an ammeter *in* the line and putting a voltmeter *across* the terminals of the motor (Fig. 48–1), we can measure the intensity of the current I and the electromotive force E. Then

$$P \text{ (watts)} = E \text{ (volts)} \times I \text{ (amperes)}.$$

* Three or four students may well work together on this experiment.

To get the mechanical **output,** we may make a **brake test.**
A very simple form of brake consists of a belt or cord passing
under a pulley on the motor shaft
and attached to two spring balances, as shown in figure 48–2.
If the motor rotates clockwise, as
indicated, it is evident that the
spring balance *A* will have to
exert more force than balance *B*
because of the friction of the
pulley on the cord. The amount
of this friction is equal to the
difference between the readings
of *A* and *B*. It is exerted each
minute through a distance equal
to the circumference of the pulley times the revolutions per
minute. The *work done in one*
minute is equal to the *friction times the distance per minute.*

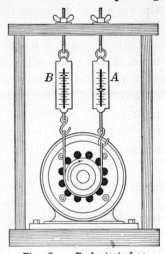

Fig. 48–2.   Brake test of an
electric motor.

We may express this output in watts by remembering
that 1 horsepower = 33,000 foot-pounds per minute = 746
watts. Therefore

$$\text{output (watts)} = \frac{\text{circum. (ft.)} \times \text{r.p.m.} \times \text{friction (lbs.)}}{33,000} \times 746.$$

$$\text{Then the efficiency} = \frac{\text{output}}{\text{input}}.$$

Directions. First determine the circumference of the
pulley by measuring the length of fine wire or thread required
to make one turn around the pulley.

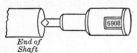

End of
Shaft

Fig. 48–3.   Counting revolutions.

To determine the number of revolutions per minute (r.p.m.), hold a
speed counter (Fig. 48–3) against the
end of the motor shaft for half a
minute and then double the number recorded.

Connect a small shunt-wound motor M to some supply of direct current. Insert the ammeter A *in* the line and the voltmeter V *across* the terminals of the motor, as shown in figure 48–1. It is well to use a double-pole switch S with a suitable rheostat R in the line to control the rush of current when starting the motor.

Before closing the switch to start the motor, let the instructor inspect and approve your arrangement of the apparatus. In starting the motor, first turn the rheostat arm in order to throw in the resistance. As the motor speeds up, gradually cut out the starting resistance. *Why?*

Put on the load by increasing the tension on the brake band. This slows down the motor a little. Keeping this pull steady, get the speed of the motor and at the same time read the spring balances, the ammeter, and the voltmeter.

Repeat the experiment, putting more load on the motor by pulling more strongly on the balances. Finally, make a third trial with still more load on the motor. It would be interesting to make these tests at half load, at full load, and at 50 per cent overload as rated on the name plate.

Record the data and results in some convenient tabular form.

Results. Compute in each trial the electrical power put in, expressed in watts; also the mechanical power got out, expressed in watts; and then the efficiency, expressed as per cent.

Why does the intensity of the current supplied to the motor change as the brake load increases?

Why cannot a motor have an efficiency of 100 per cent?

Does the efficiency of the motor change under different loads?

* * * *

Making an efficiency curve. It will be interesting to determine experimentally the efficiency of the shunt motor under several other loads and then to plot a characteristic curve. Lay off the varying loads horizontally and the efficiencies vertically. Then connect the points as far as possible with a smooth curve. Note the efficiency at *normal* load (name plate) and the load giving the maximum efficiency.

EXPERIMENT 49

POWER USED AND COST IN OPERATING ELECTRICAL APPLIANCES

I. *How can we measure the electrical power by means of a voltmeter and an ammeter?*

II. *How can we compute the cost of operating various electrical appliances?*

Voltmeter (0 — 150)

Ammeter (0 — 3 and 0 — 30)

If d-c. service is available, use d-c. instruments; if a-c. service is available, use a-c. instruments.

Electric lamps (25, 50, and 75 watts)

Electric toaster

Electric flatiron

Introduction. Electric appliances, such as lamps, toasters, and flatirons, are rated according to the **power** which they use. Electrical power is measured in watts.

$$\text{Watts} = \text{volts} \times \text{amperes}$$

This equation applies to all d-c. service and to a-c. service *provided* there is no inductance in the appliance. In the case of a vacuum cleaner, the motor does have inductance in its windings and therefore a wattmeter would be required in order to get the power consumed.

To find out the amount of electrical **energy** used, we must know not only the power (watts) but also the time (hours).

$$\text{Watt-hours} = \text{watts} \times \text{hours}$$
$$\text{Kilowatt-hours} = \frac{\text{watts} \times \text{hours}}{1000}.$$

When we buy electricity, we pay our bills according to the kilowatt-hours of electrical energy used. Therefore we must know the price of electricity. This varies in different communities from 10 cents down to 1 cent, according to the cost of generating electricity and transmitting it to the consumer. Therefore we may state that

$$\text{Cost} = \frac{\text{watts}}{1000} \times \text{hours} \times \text{rate}.$$

Directions. Arrange the electric circuit as shown in figure 49–1 so that the various appliances can be inserted

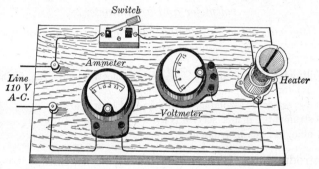

Fig. 49–1. Measuring the power used by an electric heater.

by means of a lamp socket. It is well to have a fuse plug (10 amperes) and a knife switch in the circuit. Be sure that the ammeter is *in series* with the appliance and that the voltmeter is *across* (in parallel with) the appliance. The connecting wire should be No. 14 copper wire.

Connect a 25-watt lamp in the socket and read the voltmeter and ammeter. Record these readings at once in tabular form. Repeat, using 50-watt and 75-watt lamps. It will be interesting to have different students bring various electrical heating appliances from home for this experiment. But it will be necessary to determine the current-carrying capacity of the laboratory circuits in order not "to blow the fuses."

Data

APPLIANCE	VOLTS (E)	AMPERES (I)	WATTS (EI)	COST PER HOUR (CTS.)
25-watt lamp . .				
50-watt lamp . .				
75-watt lamp . .				
Toaster				
Flatiron				

Local rate charged for electricity . . . .   cents/kw.-hr.

Results.   (1) *What is the unit of electrical power?*

(2) *How can the power used by an electrical heating appliance be measured?*

(3) *How does the maker of an electrical appliance control the power used on a 115-volt line?*

(4) *What are some of the factors which determine the rate charged for electricity in your locality?*

*   *   *   *

Optional experiment.   If a wattmeter is available, it will be interesting to measure the power used by certain electric motors found in the household — such as a vacuum cleaner, sewing machine, washing machine, and electric refrigerator.

Compute the cost of operating each appliance for one hour. The electric refrigerator is not running continuously and just how much of the time it is running depends on its construction (heat insulation) and location. *How could one measure the electricity used in such intermittent service?*

SOUND

BLOCK VII. SOUND WAVES AND MUSIC

Suggestive Questions

1. *Can you hear sounds made under water?*
2. *If an alarm clock goes off under a vacuum jar, can you hear it?*
3. *What is meant by the wave length of a sound?*
4. *How could you prove that light travels faster than sound?*
5. *What is the difference between noise and a musical note?*
6. *What enables one to recognize a voice over the telephone?*
7. *What is the function of the sounding box of a violin?*
8. *If one tightens a violin string, does he raise or lower the pitch?*
9. *Why should a piano when once in tune get out of tune?*
10. *Why is a megaphone effective in a crew race?*
11. *Can a tone be pitched so high that no one can hear it?*
12. *How does the pitch of the sound made by an electric fan depend upon the speed?*
13. *Why is it harder to speak to a crowd out of doors than indoors?*
14. *How does a violin, with only four strings, produce as many notes as a piano, which has at least 88 strings?*
15. *How could you determine the pitch of a whistle which consists of a tube closed at one end?*
16. *How far away does a brick wall have to be in order that we may perceive an echo?*
17. *Why are phonograph records reproduced more accurately by means of a radio receiving set than by a purely mechanical method?*

EXPERIMENT 50

FREQUENCY OF A TUNING FORK

How many vibrations does a tuning fork make in one second?

Tuning fork with stylus attached	Clock or stop watch
Recording apparatus (Fig. 50–1)	Gum camphor
Glass plates	Clamp for releasing tuning fork

Introduction. Since a tuning fork, which gives a musical sound, vibrates too fast for direct counting by the eye, it is necessary to use a special apparatus, such as is shown in

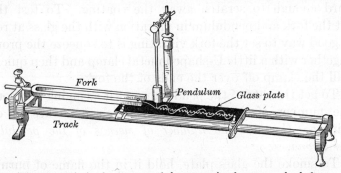

Fig. 50–1. A simple chronograph for measuring frequency of a fork.

figure 50–1. This very simple **chronograph** consists of three parts: a smoked glass plate or paper,* a tuning fork with a fine-wire or paper stylus attached to one prong, and a short pendulum which also has a wire stylus projecting so as to

---

* If the tracings are made on smoked paper, they may easily be "fixed" by pouring over the smoked surface a very thin solution of shellac. After a few minutes the paper is dry and may be pasted in the notebook as a part of the record of the experiment.

Since smoked glass is always more or less dirty, the glass is sometimes covered with a thin coat of whiting in alcohol or of "Bon Ami" soap.

touch the glass plate. The smoked-glass plate is drawn along a straight track beneath the stylus of the vibrating tuning fork and at right angles to the direction of the vibrations so that it makes a wavy curve on the glass. At the same time the pendulum point swings back and forth across this curve. If, then, we know the number of complete swings of the pendulum per second and count on the smoked glass the number of vibrations of the fork corresponding to one complete swing of the pendulum, we can easily compute the number of vibrations of the tuning fork per second.

Directions. Clamp the tuning fork so that its tracing point is only a few millimeters from the point of the pendulum. The line of these two tracing points should be parallel to the track on which the glass is to move. The tracing points must rest lightly on the smoked-glass surface and yet hard enough to scratch away the coating. To test this, set the fork and pendulum in vibration with the glass at rest. A good way to set the fork vibrating is to squeeze the prongs together with a little U-shaped metal clamp and then quickly pull the clamp off over the ends of the fork.

To get the rate of the pendulum, set it swinging and count the number of complete swings which it makes in one minute. *Compute the number of swings of the pendulum per second.*

To smoke the glass plate, hold it in the flame of burning gum camphor. Keep the plate moving back and forth in order not to crack it by overheating. Place the plate, smoked side up, on the slider and adjust the two styluses.

When the apparatus is properly adjusted, start the pendulum swinging, set the fork vibrating, and then draw the glass along the track at such a rate as to have at least one *complete* swing of the pendulum recorded on the glass. Several sets of tracings may be recorded on the same plate by moving it a little to one side and so bringing a fresh surface under the tracing points.

Next, count the number of vibrations of the fork corresponding to a complete swing of the pendulum, *i.e.*, the number of vibrations traced by the fork between the points A and C (Fig. 50–2) or between B and D, estimating in every case to tenths of a vibration.

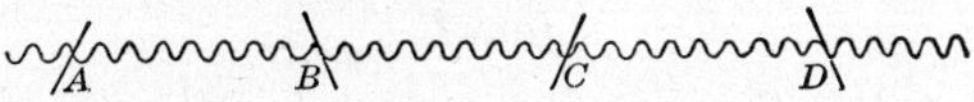

Fig. 50–2.   Curves of tuning fork and pendulum.

Make at least three tracings and on each tracing count the number of vibrations of the tuning fork corresponding to a complete swing of the pendulum. *Take the mean of these counts as the number of vibrations of the fork to one of the pendulum.*

Compute the number of complete vibrations made by the tuning fork per second.

*   *   *   *

Making a permanent record. The tracing on the smoked glass can be fixed by spraying on it a very thin solution of shellac. Prints can now be easily made on blue-print paper or on photographic paper, such as Velox, and developed and fixed. These records can then be pasted in the notebook.

WAVE LENGTH. VELOCITY OF SOUND IN AIR

I. *How long is the sound wave emitted by a vibrating tuning fork?*

II. *How fast does the sound wave travel in the air of the room?*

2 Tuning forks of known frequency but of different pitch (256, 512)	Large flat stopper
	Meter stick
Hydrometer jar of water	Rubber bands
Resonating tube	

Introduction. If a tuning fork is set in vibration and held in front of a column of air (Fig. 51–1), the loudness of its note will be greatly increased, provided that the air column is of such a length as *to vibrate in sympathy* with the fork. Such an air column is said to be in **resonance** with the fork. Examples of the use of resonant air columns are to be found in fifes, trombones, cornets, and organ pipes.

This phenomenon may be explained on the theory of the combination of direct and reflected waves. Suppose a prong of the fork begins to move *inward*. It starts a wave (condensation) along the tube. If this impulse, or wave, can travel to the end of the tube and back again just in time to meet the prong as it starts to move *outward*, then the two waves combine and produce a louder tone. Since this condensation has traveled to the end of the air column and back during a half-vibration of the tuning fork, the distance in and out must be equal to half a wave length, or *the distance one way is equal to a quarter of a wave length*. Experiments show that the distance actually traveled by the impulse in going each way is a little greater than the length of the air column on account of the reflection from the sides and the spreading at the open end. The correction to be added is equal to about one-quarter of the inside diameter of the tube. Therefore the length of the sound wave emitted by the tuning fork is four times the sum of the length of the air column and one-fourth of its diameter.

This wave length multiplied by the number of vibrations per second (Exp. 50) gives the distance which the sound travels in the air in one second at the temperature of the room.

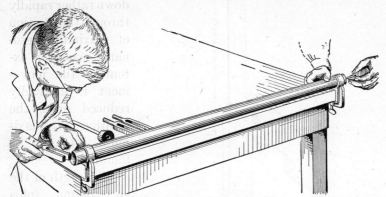

Fig. 51–1. Resonance tube (brass), according to W. C. Sabine. The length can be varied by means of a plunger at the right.

Directions. Place a glass tube in the hydrometer jar and pour in enough water nearly to fill the jar. Strike one prong of the tuning fork on a large rubber stopper and hold the vibrating fork over the open end of the tube, as shown in figure 51–2. By slowly raising the tube out of the water, a point will be found where the air column is of just the right length to reinforce the fork. Mark with a rubber band around the tube the position of the surface of the water where the sound was loudest. Then set the fork in vibration again and by raising and lowering the tube and listening intently, determine again as precisely as you can the point where the air column gives the greatest reinforcement. Measure the length of the air column.

In this experiment the settings for obtaining the data are more or less indefinite and therefore one trial may be far from the true value. To reduce the probable error, make several trials and take the mean. Experience has shown that a more accurate setting can be obtained if the tube is moved up and down rather rapidly through the position of maximum resonance, while the extent of the movement is gradually reduced until the position of maximum intensity is found.

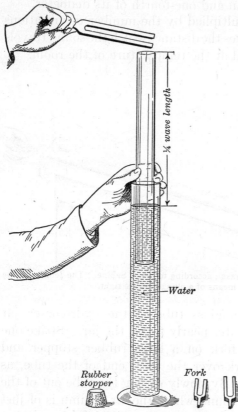

Fig. 51-2. Finding the length of a resonating air column.

The length of the air column (plus about 0.25 of the internal diameter of the tube) is equal to *one-fourth* the wave length of the tone of the fork in air. *Compute the wave length of the sound emitted by the tuning fork.*

Given the frequency of the fork, *i.e.,* the number of vibrations per second, *compute the velocity of sound at the temperature of the room,* using the wave length just determined.

* * * *

If time permits, repeat the experiment, using a tuning fork of some other frequency.

It is also possible to find a second position of the water surface nearer the bottom of the tube which also gives reinforcement to the sound. The difference between the length of the short and long air columns is equal to *one-half* a wave length.

It is usually stated that the velocity of sound in air is 331 meters per second at 0° C. and that it increases about 0.6 meter per second for each degree C. rise. Compare this calculated value for the velocity of sound with the result of your experiment and compute the percentage error.

EXPERIMENT 52

VIBRATING STRINGS

I. *How is the rate of vibration of a stretched wire affected by its length?*

II. *How is the rate of vibration of a stretched wire affected by the tension?*

Monochord with a steel wire (#26 B. & S.)   Set of heavy weights
3 Tuning forks (256, 384, and 512)   Meter stick

Introduction. We are all more or less familiar with certain stringed musical instruments, such as the violin, the harp, and the piano. The violin has four strings, three made of plain gut and the fourth of gut wound with fine wire. The violinist changes the length of the vibrating string with his fingers and in the preliminary tuning of the instrument he adjusts the tension on each string. Thus, by applying a few simple physical principles in regard to vibrating strings, he is able to produce a marvelous variety of musical tones. In this experiment we shall learn that the pitch of the musical note produced by a vibrating string depends upon its length and its tension.

Directions. I. _Effect of length._ Stretch a steel wire along the monochord box (Fig. 52–1) and move the bridge B so that its distance from the fixed end A is about 60 centimeters. Adjust the tension on the wire until the note given by the wire when plucked in the middle is in unison with the note of the lowest fork (256).

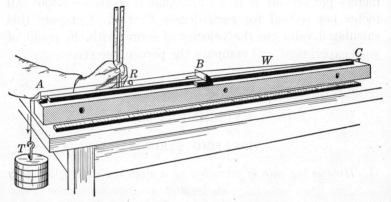

Fig. 52–1. Finding the frequency of steel wire.

This unison can best be detected by the absence of **beats.** When two notes are nearly but not quite in unison, they at one moment reinforce and at the next interfere with each other, and the sound is alternately loud and faint. These pulsations, known as beats, furnish a mechanical method for securing unison. The beats cannot be detected until the wire and the fork are nearly in unison. But when once they are detected, the length of the wire should be varied so as to make the beats succeed each other more and more slowly until finally they seem to disappear. The sound of the fork may be greatly reinforced by holding its shank on the monochord box. Then the beats can be felt by resting the fingers lightly on the board.*

* When several monochords are sounding in the same room, it may be very difficult to detect beats. Another method of showing resonance is to put a small paper rider on the wire near its midpoint. When the base of the vibrat-

(*a*) Measure carefully the length of the wire between A and B. Record the pitch of the tuning fork (its number).

(*b*) Keeping the tension on the wire the same, move the bridge B until the note of the vibrating wire AB is exactly in unison with the fork 512, which is an octave higher than the first one. Measure the length of the vibrating wire between A and B. Record this with the pitch of the fork.

(*c*) Again vary the length of the vibrating wire so as to bring it into unison with a third fork, such as 384, the fifth note above middle C. Measure and record the length of the vibrating wire.

Compare the measured lengths of the vibrating wire with the vibration numbers as marked on the forks. State the law concerning the rate of a vibrating string and its length when the tension is kept constant.

II. *Effect of tension.*

(*a*) Put the bridge B at the same distance from A (about 60 centimeters) as in the first trial. Adjust the tension in the wire so that the plucked wire gives a musical note at about middle C. Take great care to bring the wire and the C fork, 256, into exact unison by adjusting the tension. *Record the tension on the wire by counting the weights; also record the pitch* (number) *of the fork.*

(*b*) Adjust the tension on the wire so that the wire and the C' fork, 512, are in unison. *Record this value of the tension and the number of the C' fork.*

What is the ratio between the tensions on the wire in these two trials? What is the ratio of the square roots of the tensions?

What is the ratio between the vibration rates in the two trials?

In order to double the rate of vibration, by what must we multiply the tension?

What would be the frequency of No. 26 steel wire 60 cm. long and under 9 kg. tension?

ing fork rests on the monochord, the paper rider will jump off if the wire and the fork have the same pitch.

*   *   *   *

Effect of the mass of the wire. A third factor which controls the pitch of a vibrating wire is its mass per centimeter of length. With the same kind of steel, the masses per unit length of two different wires will vary directly as the squares of the diameters. Find as before the length of a No. 24 (B. & S.) steel piano wire which will produce 256 vibrations per second under a tension of 9 kilograms. From the law of frequency and length (I), compute the frequency of No. 24 steel wire 60 cm. long and under 9 kg. tension. Measure with micrometer caliper the diameters of No. 26 and No. 24 wires and then compare the ratio of the frequencies (assuming the length and tension to be constant) with the inverse ratio of the diameters.

LIGHT

BLOCK VIII. LIGHT WAVES AND THEIR USES

Suggestive Questions

1. *Why is a parobolic reflector better for an automobile headlight than a spherical one?*

2. *How can a glass prism act as a reflector?*

3. *Why do objects in water appear to be nearer the surface than they really are?*

4. *How far from a lens does anything have to be in order to be called a "distant object"?*

5. *What is meant by a virtual image?*

6. *What is an international candle?*

7. *What does wave length have to do with the color of light?*

8. *What reason have we for believing that there is invisible light?*

9. *Why does the color of a fabric depend upon the kind of artificial light used?*

10. *What practical use is there for the compound microscope?*

11. *Why have men measured the speed of light with such great precision?*

12. *In what ways does the illumination of streets and highways involve a question of public safety?*

13. *Does light always travel in straight lines?*

14. *What sort of mirror would be used to throw a real image on a screen?*

15. *Can a person see his full-length image in a plane mirror which is one-half as tall as he is?*

EXPERIMENT 53

ILLUMINATION. THE FOOT-CANDLE METER

*What is the intensity of illumination in various parts of the
laboratory or class room?*

Foot-candle meter (Weston Electric Instrument Company's
or General Electric Company's)

Introduction. We must have light in order to see things.
Good eyes are useless unless we have adequate illumination.
We are slowly coming to realize the importance of the right

Fig. 53–1. Foot-candle meter
(Weston Junior).

sort of lighting, not only for efficiency
and safety in industry and in trans-
portation but also for the conserva-
tion of eyesight. Since the luminous
intensity of lamps varies enormously,
we need a unit of luminous intensity.
For many years a sperm candle was
taken as the unit, but it was very
difficult to define the exact specifica-
tions of a standard candle. At present the **international candle,** which
is accepted in England, France, and
the United States, is established by
a set of standard incandescent lamps
maintained, for this country, at the
National Bureau of Standards in
Washington, D. C. Thus we speak
of a certain lamp as having a certain candle power, meaning
that it is equivalent to a certain number of international
candles.

The unit quantity of light cast upon a surface, that is, the unit of illumination, is the **foot-candle.** This is the *illumination on a surface which is one foot from a standard candle.* The modern foot-candle meter reads directly the intensity of illumination at a given place. The instrument consists essentially of a photoelectric cell and a galvanometer. The light falling upon a specially prepared metal plate generates an electric current (very tiny) directly proportional to the light which strikes it. The galvanometer scale is calibrated to read foot-candles. Such instruments are delicate and expensive and so should be handled with great care.

Fig. 53-2. Foot-candle meter (General Electric Co.).

In one form (Weston, Fig. 53-1) the sensitive plate and the scale are side by side, and in another form (General Electric, Fig. 53-2) the plate is on top and the scale is on the side.

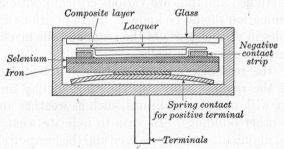

Fig. 53-2. Diagram of cross section.

The intensity of illumination which we have to measure varies from several thousand foot-candles out of doors on a bright, clear, summer day to less than five foot-candles in corridors, theaters, and churches.   For this reason foot-candle meters sometimes have two or three scales (Fig. 53–3) to cover the high and low ranges of intensities of illumination.   *Always* set the instrument switch for "high" to see what is the approximate range of illumination to be measured;   then switch to the lower scale if it will carry the illumination.   It is well to turn the switch to the "off" position or to put the instrument in its case when it is not in use.

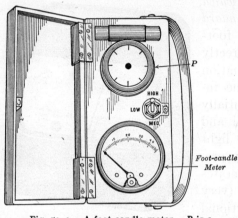

Fig. 53–3.   A foot-candle meter.   *P* is a "photronic" cell.

Directions.   First make yourself perfectly familiar with the instrument by reading the directions which come with it. Then make a sketch of the room in which the illumination is to be studied and indicate various critical positions where the illumination should be known.   Such positions are desks and tables in various parts of the room and the blackboards, maps, and charts on the walls.

Place the readings of your instrument directly on your plan of the room.   Note also the time of day and date, together with outside conditions, such as weather and nearness to other buildings.   Be sure to indicate what kind of artificial illumination, if any, is used and the location and kind of lamps used.

Results.   Finally, discuss the illumination of the room which you have studied and make some recommendations on how it can be improved.

EXPERIMENT 54

PHOTOMETERS. MEASUREMENT OF CANDLE POWER

I. *What is the candle power of a given electric-lamp bulb in terms of a standard lamp?*

II. *What is the commercial efficiency (lumens per watt) of the lamp?*

Bunsen photometer in a darkened room or in a light-tight box
Two incandescent lamps (one of known candle power)

Voltmeter (0 — 150 volts)
Ammeter (0 — 3 amp.)
Shade for electric bulb

Introduction. As we have just seen, the proper illumination of our streets, factories, and homes is a matter of vital importance; but it is by no means a simple one. The first factor to be considered is the **luminous intensity** of the lamp itself, and this, we learned, is measured by comparison with the international candle.

The instrument used to compare a standard lamp with some other the intensity of which we wish to measure is called a **photometer**. In this experiment we shall describe a Bunsen "grease-spot" photometer because it is very simple and easy to operate. Essentially it is a white paper screen with a translucent spot in the center. This screen is placed between the lamps to be compared so that one side is lighted by one lamp and one by the other. The screen is moved back and forth between the lamps until it is equally illuminated on both sides. In this position the spot disappears, or at least looks equally bright on both sides.

Experience shows that the illumination on a book decreases as one moves away from the lamp. In fact, it can be proved that *the intensity of illumination varies inversely as the square of the distance.* Thus, a 16-candle-power lamp will

213

illuminate a surface placed 1 foot from it with an intensity of *16 foot-candles*. But if the book were 2 feet from the lamp, the intensity of illumination would be $\frac{16}{4}$, or 4 foot-candles. In general,

Illumination (foot-candles) $= \dfrac{\textbf{candle power}}{\textbf{distance squared (ft.}^2)}.$

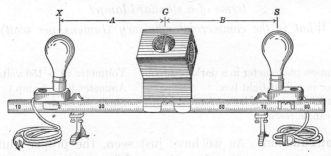

Fig. 54–1. Bunsen photometer used to compare lamp X with a standard lamp S.

Suppose that the lamp X (Fig. 54–1) to be tested is A feet from the screen of a Bunsen photometer, and that the standard lamp S equally illuminates the screen when B feet away.

Then
$$\frac{X}{A^2} = \frac{S}{B^2}$$

or
$$\frac{X}{S} = \frac{A^2}{B^2}.$$

Stated in words, *the candle powers of the two lamps are directly proportional to the squares of their distances from the screen.* Thus, knowing S and measuring A and B, we can compute X.

Directions. Set up a Bunsen photometer in a darkened room or in a light-tight box, as shown in figure 54–1. Use a standard electric lamp S as a basis for comparison. Insert a rheostat in the power circuit so as to bring the standard lamp to its required voltage. At the other end of the photometer bar (about 200 centimeters from the first lamp) set up the other electric lamp X which is to be tested. Between these two lamps place the photometer box or screen G with the grease spot. This screen is to be moved back and forth between the lights until a position is found at which the screen is equally illuminated on both sides. This means that the central spot or disk and the surrounding rim of paper should be of the same

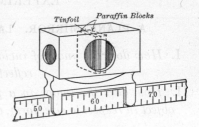

Fig. 54-2.   Joly paraffin-block box.

brightness. Since it is difficult to set this sight box or screen precisely right, several trials should be made and the average position taken.*

Find the candle power of an ordinary tungsten (Mazda B) *lamp;* that is, the **mean horizontal candle power.** From the readings of the voltmeter and ammeter in the lamp circuit, *compute the lumens per watt* (commercial efficiency).

Measure the candle power of a gas-filled tungsten (Mazda C) lamp and *compute its commercial efficiency.*

Finally, if time permits, turn the incandescent lamp so that its axis is in a horizontal position and *measure its candle power downward* (along the axis) *both with and without a shade.*

---

* Another type of photometer (Fig. 54–2), known as the Joly photometer, consists of a sight box containing two paraffin blocks separated by a metallic diaphragm instead of the grease-spot screen.

EXPERIMENT 55

A PLANE MIRROR. LAWS OF REFLECTION

I. *How does the angle of incidence compare with the angle of reflection?*

II. *How does the image in a plane mirror compare with the object in respect to size, form, and distance from the mirror?*

Plane mirror	Paper
Block for holding mirror	Protractor
Pins	Rule

Introduction. The ancients used mirrors which consisted merely of brightly polished metallic surfaces. Most of the mirrors which we use are made of glass coated with a layer of metal on the back side. In this way the metallic surface remains bright.

Have you ever stopped to think where your image appears to be as you looked into a mirror? Does it seem to be on the glass, behind the mirror, or in front of the mirror? Perhaps you have used a small mirror to reflect the sunlight into someone's eyes. Do you know just how to place your mirror in order to reflect the light in any particular direction? Doubtless you have read about the use of the periscope in warfare. Did you know that it consists essentially of two plane mirrors placed in a certain way in a tube?

In this experiment we shall learn just how a plane mirror reflects light and just where the image seen in such a mirror appears to be.

Directions. I. *Reflection by a plane mirror.* Draw a straight line across the middle of a sheet of paper and label this the **Mirror line.** Set up the mirror so that its reflecting surface is exactly over this line. At a distance of 10–15 centimeters in front of the mirror, make a dot and label it *O.*

Place a pin so that it stands directly on this dot. To locate the image of this pin, lay a straight edge (rule) on the paper so that it points directly at the image. Care should be taken *to sight* with only one eye along the edge of the rule. Then draw a clean, sharp line along this edge that points toward the image. To make sure that the rule has not

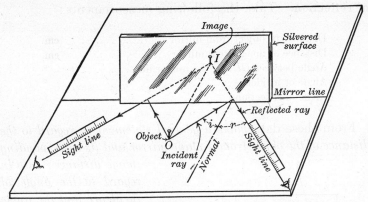

Fig. 55-1. Reflection in a plane mirror.

slipped in the process, remove the rule and look along the surface of the paper to see if the line really does point at the image. If not, erase the line and try again.

Place the rule on the other side of the object-pin O. Draw another *sight line* just as before, making sure that the mirror still has its reflecting surface just on the mirror line. Repeat this process, drawing several sight lines.

Now remove the mirror and block. Continue each of the sight lines as solid lines up to the mirror line and then continue them as dotted lines behind the mirror until they meet. Mark this point of intersection I, the image-point. The solid sight lines represent **reflected rays.** From the object-point O draw lines to the intersection of each of these sight lines with the mirror line. These lines from O to the mirror represent the **incident rays.** Connect the object-point O with the image-point I, making the line solid in front of the mirror and dotted behind the mirror. Indicate the direction in which light travels along the lines by arrows, as shown in figure 55–1.

At one of the points of reflection erect a **normal**, that is, a perpendicular to the mirror. Label the angle between the incident ray and the normal the **angle of incidence**. Label the angle between the reflected ray and the normal the **angle of reflection**. Take the following measurements:

Distance of object from mirror . . . . cm.
Distance of image from mirror . . . . . . cm.
Angle between *OI* and the mirror line . . . . °
Angle of incidence . . . . °
Angle of reflection . . . . °

From these data *make a general statement in regard to the distance of the object from a plane mirror and its corresponding image distance; also in regard to the angle of incidence and the angle of reflection.*

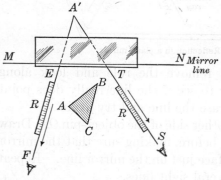

Fig. 55–2. Finding the image of the triangle *ABC*.

II. *Image formed by a plane mirror.* On another sheet of paper draw a line across the middle and set up the mirror as before. Draw a triangle (about 5 cm. on each side) and label it *ABC*, as shown in figure 55–2. By drawing two sight lines at each point, locate the image-points of *A*, *B*, and *C*, and label these points *A′*, *B′*, and *C′*. Construct with dotted lines the image of *ABC*. Measure the lengths of *A′B′*, *B′C′*, and *A′C′*, and compare them with the corresponding object-lines. If the paper is folded along the mirror line and if the work has been carefully done, the image will be found to coincide very closely (within 1 or

2 mm.) with the object when the paper is held to the light.
If the first trial is not satisfactory, repeat the experiment.

*Compare the object with its image formed by a plane mirror
in respect to size, distance, and form.*

* * * *

Multiple images. Some very curious effects can be got
by using two or more plane mirrors and so producing double
or triple reflections. Set
up two plane mirrors
to form a right angle
(Fig. 55–3). Locate by
sight lines the position of
the three images of any
object placed in the open
space between the mir-
rors. Move the mirrors
so as to form an angle of
60° and count the num-
ber of images. Then
make an angle of 45° and

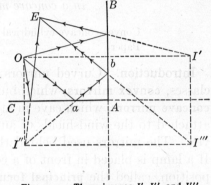

Fig. 55–3. Three images *I'*, *I''*, and *I'''*
formed by two mirrors at right angles.

count the number of images. *State a rule which will tell you
the number of images formed by two mirrors at any angle.*

Set up two plane mirrors in such a way as to illustrate the
principle of the periscope.

EXPERIMENT 56

IMAGES FORMED BY CURVED MIRRORS

I. *What are the position, size, and shape of an image formed in a convex mirror?*

II. *What are the position, size, and shape of an image formed in a concave mirror?*

Convex-concave cylindrical mirror	Rule
Paper	Pins

Introduction. Curved mirrors may be divided into two classes, **convex mirrors,** which bulge out in the middle, and **concave mirrors,** which cave in at the middle. The mirrors attached to the windshields of automobiles are usually convex. The mirrors used behind the headlights are concave. If a lamp is placed in front of a concave mirror at a certain position, called the **principal focus,** the light is reflected in parallel rays. The distance of the principal focus from the mirror is called the **focal length** of the mirror. If the mirror is spherical, or part of the inside surface of a hollow sphere, its *focal length is almost one-half the radius of curvature.* If the lamp is placed nearer to the mirror than the principal focus, the reflected rays are divergent. If the lamp is placed farther from the mirror than the focus, the reflected rays are convergent. In this experiment we shall find out just where the reflected rays converge to a point, called the **image point.** We shall also learn much about the size and shape of the images formed by both concave and convex mirrors and why each type of mirror is especially well adapted for certain purposes.

The principles involved in curved mirrors can be conveniently studied in cylindrical mirrors. In this experiment we shall stand the cylindrical mirror so that its straight edges are vertical and its curved edges are parallel with the table. The mirror itself is merely a section of brass pipe nickel-plated in order to serve both as a concave and a convex cylindrical mirror.

Directions. I. *Convex mirror.* Place on a sheet of paper a convex cylindrical mirror so that its straight lines are vertical. Then trace on the paper the position of its convex surface. About 5 centimeters in front of the mirror draw as object an arrow 6 centimeters long labeled *ABC*, somewhat as shown in figure 56–1. To locate the position of the image of *A*, place a pin at point *A* so that it stands erect. Then draw two sight lines along the edge of a rule (one on each side of the pin) pointing at the image of the pin. Label each of these lines *A*. Then stand the pin at *B* and draw, as before, two sight lines toward the image. In the same way draw sight lines to locate the image of *C*.

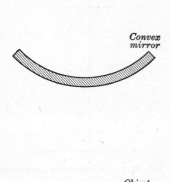

Fig. 56–1.   Convex cylindrical mirror.

Remove the mirror and pin. Continue each pair of sight lines until they intersect. In this way locate the image-points of *A*, *B*, and *C* and label these points *A'*, *B'*, *C'*. Draw a straight line from *A'* to *B'* and from *B'* to *C'* with an arrowhead at *A'*. Label this arrow the **Image.**

Draw a dotted line from *A* to *A'*, from *B* to *B'*, and from *C* to *C'*. Prolong these lines until they intersect.

Compare the object and its image in a convex mirror as to position, size, and shape.

II. *Concave mirror.* Stand the mirror a little above the middle of a sheet of paper and draw a sharp line along its concave edge. Remove the mirror and draw a dotted line connecting the ends of the arc. Draw a perpendicular at the midpoint of this chord and label it **axis**. Assuming that

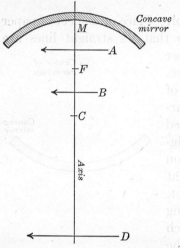

Fig. 56-2. Concave cylindrical mirror.

the radius of curvature is 5 centimeters, mark the **center of curvature** with the letter *C*. Mark the **focus** *F*, which is halfway between the center of curvature *C* and the mirror *M*, as shown in figure 56-2. In order to locate the images of objects at varying positions along the axis, draw a short arrow between *F* and *M* and label it *A*, another between *F* and *C* and label it *B*, and a third beyond *C* and label it *D*, somewhat as shown in the figure.

Replace the concave mirror on its line and observe the direction, curvature, and relative length of the images of *A* and *B*. In order to see these images more distinctly, it will be useful to draw an arrow on a small strip of paper and fold up one end so that the arrow is on the vertical part, as shown in figure 56-3. Now place this strip of paper first over *A* and then over *B*. *Do the images of A and B point in the same direction as the objects?*

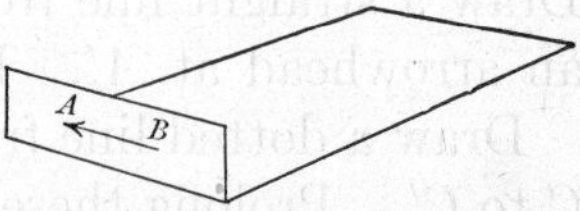

To locate the position of the image of *A*, stand a pin upright at the *midpoint* of *A* and draw two

Fig. 56-3. Arrow on paper.

sight lines directly at its image. Label these lines *A*, *A*. Locate the images of *B* and *D* in the same way.

When an image seems to be back of a mirror, it is said to be **virtual** because the rays of light do not actually come from the image point but simply look as if they had come from it.   On the other hand, when as in some cases with a concave mirror the image is found in front of the mirror, it is said to be a **real image** because the rays actually do pass through the image point.

Fold the two sheets of paper which you have used for this experiment and paste them neatly in your notebook as a part of your record of the experiment.

Make clear, concise statements in answer to the following questions :

(1) *Where must the object be placed in order to get a virtual image and where to get a real image?*

(2) *Where must the object be placed in order to get an image pointing in the same direction as the object and where to get a reversed image?*

(3) *Where must the object be placed in order to get an image which is smaller than the object and where to get a larger image?*

*   *   *   *

Concave spherical mirror.   Measure the focal length f of a small concave spherical mirror by getting the image of the sun upon a narrow strip of paper held in front of the mirror.

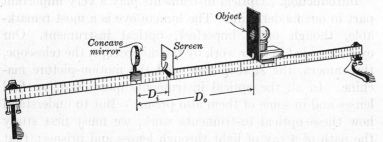

Fig. 56–4. Concave spherical mirror used to form a real image on the screen.

The focus is the place where the spot of light is smallest and brightest.

In a darkened room place a wire netting illuminated by a small electric lamp as the object at a distance of about three times the focal length from the mirror. Find the position of the image by letting it fall on a cardboard screen (Fig. 56–4). Measure the distance of the object from the center of the mirror D_o and the corresponding distance of the image D_i. *Compute the focal length f from the equation*

$$\frac{1}{f} = \frac{1}{D_o} + \frac{1}{D_i}.$$

Compare this value of the focal length with that obtained by using the sun as the object.

EXPERIMENT 57

REFRACTION OF LIGHT BY GLASS

I. *How is a ray of light bent in passing from glass into air?*
II. *What is the relation between the speed of light in air and in glass?*

Rectangular glass plate   Protractor
Paper   Pins
Rule

Introduction. Optical instruments play a very important part in our modern life. The human eye is a most remarkable, though often imperfect, optical instrument. Our eyes are aided in their work by the microscope, the telescope, the camera, the stereopticon, and the motion-picture machine. In all the optical instruments mentioned, we find lenses and in some of them also prisms. But to understand how these optical instruments work, we must first study the path of a ray of light through lenses and prisms; that is, the **refraction** of light by glass.

We all know that a stick standing obliquely in water appears to be broken at the water's surface. We are also familiar with the shoaling effect of water, which makes a rock or a fish in the water always seem to be nearer the surface than it really is.   These phenomena are but examples of the refraction, or bending, of light as it passes from water into air.

The reason for the refraction of light was not understood until the velocity of light in different substances had been

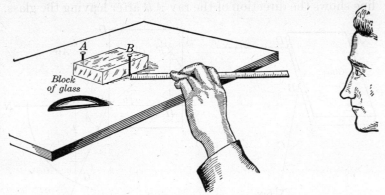

Fig. 57-1.   Refraction by a block of glass.

measured.   In this experiment we shall learn how to determine the amount that a beam of light is bent in passing from glass into air.

Directions.   Lay a rectangular block of glass on a sheet of paper in the position shown in figure 57–1.   Trace with a sharp pencil the edge of the glass.   Stand a pin upright at A and touching the edge of the glass and another pin B touching the opposite edge.

If one places his eye on a level with the paper and looks *into* the edge DE (Fig. 57–2), the portion of the pin A seen through the glass seems to be in line with the part seen over the glass *only* when the eye looks into the glass in the direction FD, perpendicular to the edge DE.

In order to show just how much a ray of light is bent in passing from glass to air, move the head slowly to the left until the pin B just covers the image of pin A as seen through the glass.   Place a rule so that one edge points directly at B and at the image of A as seen through the glass. Then draw the sight line CB as shown in figure 57–2.

Remove the glass and connect the points A and B. This line represents the direction of a ray of light through the glass. Prolong the sight line until it strikes the point B. This sight line shows the direction of the ray AB after leaving the glass.

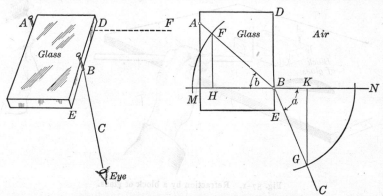

Fig. 57–2.   Finding the index of refraction of glass

If we erect a normal MN at B perpendicular to DE, *what do we find in regard to the size of the angle in air* (a) *and the angle in glass* (b)?

Index of refraction. The refraction of light in passing from glass into air depends on the relative speeds of light in glass and air. It can be proved* that *the speed of light in air is to its speed in glass as the **sine of the angle** in air is to the **sine of the angle** in glass.* The term *sine* is the mathematical name for the ratio of the opposite side to the hypotenuse of a right triangle.† Thus the sine of angle a is GK/BG (Fig. 57–2). To get the ratio of the sines of these angles, lay off on AF and BC equal distances (the longer the better), such as BF and BG, and draw FH and GK perpendicular to the normal MN. The sine of angle a is

---

* Black's *Introductory Course in College Physics*, pp. 609–610.
† For further information about sines and tangents of angles see Appendix.

GK/BG and the sine of angle b is FH/BF, but since $BF = BG$,

$$\text{Index} = \frac{\text{sine } a}{\text{sine } b} = \frac{GK}{FH}.$$

In short, to get the **index of refraction** of the glass used in this experiment, *i.e.*, *ratio of speed of light in air to speed of light in glass*, we have merely to divide the length of GK (measured to tenths of a millimeter) by the length of FH.

To make a second trial, move the position of pin A to a new point A' along the edge of the glass and repeat the experiment.

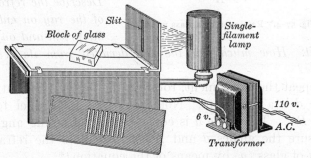

Fig. 57–3.   Refraction of a beam of light by a block of glass.

It is also interesting to measure angles a and b in degrees with a protractor and compute the index of refraction from the values of the sines given in Table XII in the Appendix.

Alternative method.   If suitable apparatus (Fig. 57–3) is available, it is interesting to perform this experiment with an actual beam of light from a single-filament lamp. The light paths can easily be marked with dots and the rest of the construction carried out as before.

*   *   *   *

Refraction by a prism.   Find the shape of the path followed by a ray of light in passing through a 60°-prism to the eye.   Set up two pins D and E on a sheet of paper and place a triangular block of glass ABC as shown in figure 57-4. Sight along a straight edge in the direction $D'E'$ so that the two pins D and E appear to be in line when seen through

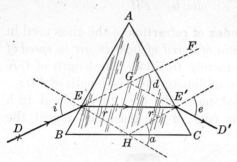

Fig. 57-4. Refraction by a glass prism.

the side AC of the prism. Remove the prism and draw line EE', the path of the ray through the prism. Construct perpendiculars at E and E' to the refracting surfaces. *Describe the refraction of the ray on entering the prism and on leaving it. How much was the ray deviated from its original course?*

Repeat the experiment, rotating the prism ABC until the angle d is a minimum. Note that EE' is parallel to the base BC. The angle a is equal to the refracting angle A. Measure the angles d and A and calculate the refractive index of glass (n) by means of the equation:*

$$n = \frac{\sin \frac{1}{2}(A + d)}{\sin \frac{1}{2}A}.$$

* The derivation of this equation is given on page 613 of BLACK's *Introductory Course in College Physics.*

EXPERIMENT 58

FOCAL LENGTH AND CONJUGATE FOCI OF A CONVERGING LENS

I. *How far is the image of a distant object from a convex lens?*

II. *What relation exists between the object-distance and the image-distance when the object is near a convex lens?*

Meter stick and supports (Fig. 58–2) Holders for lens and screen
Electric lamp with wire netting Double convex lens (f. 10–
White cardboard screen 15 cm.)

Introduction. Lenses may be divided into two classes — **concave** lenses, which have thick edges, and **convex** lenses, which have thin edges. Of these, the kind which is most commonly used in cameras, telescopes, and microscopes is the convex lens. This type is often referred to as a *converging* lens because parallel rays are converged to a fixed point, called the **principal focus.** Some of us have doubtless handled a "burning glass" (a double convex lens) in such a way that the rays from the sun entered the lens and were so bent in direction (refracted) that they converged to a point. To understand this phenomenon, we may think of two glass prisms placed with their bases together. Parallel rays passing through these prisms will be bent toward the base *BC* of each prism, as shown in Experiment 57. A double convex lens is not very different in shape from this combination of prisms, except that its surfaces are spherical instead of flat.

The distance between the principal focus and the lens is the **focal length** of the lens. An object which is 100 feet or more away sends to a lens rays that are practically parallel; that is, rays from any distant object-point to different parts of the lens are very nearly parallel. Therefore we may locate the focus by getting the image of a distant building or tree on a screen. We can then determine the focal length of the lens by measuring the distance between the lens and the image formed of the distant object.

When the object is placed nearer the lens but beyond the focus, the image is formed at a definite point (depending on the focal length) *beyond* the focus on the other side of the lens. In this experiment we shall see that whenever a real

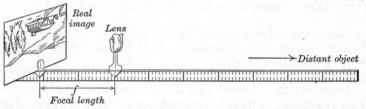

Fig. 58–1. Image of a distant object is at the principal focus.

image is formed on a screen, then the object and image may be interchanged. Two such points situated on either side of a lens so that an object at one point will form an image at the other are called **conjugate foci** of the lens. We shall also learn that an important relation exists between the distance of the object from the lens (D_o), the distance of the image from the lens (D_i), and the focal length of the lens (f).

Directions. I. *Focal length.* Set the double convex lens and the cardboard screen on a meter stick (Fig. 58–1). Place the stick in the back part of the room, pointing at some distant object out of the window. Having set the lens on one of the main divisions of the meter stick, move the screen toward and away from the lens until the most distant bright object which can be seen through the window is sharply focused on the screen, *i.e.*, forms a clear picture. Read and record the positions of lens and screen. *Compute the focal length of the lens.*

Move the lens to a new position on the stick and again make a new setting of the screen in the same way as before.

After making a third trial, find the average of the three focal lengths and record this as the focal length of the lens. Record also the number of the lens used.

II. *Relations of object and image.*   Set up the meter stick as shown in figure 58–2 so that the object (an illuminated wire netting) is away from the window.   Place the cardboard screen at the opposite end and darken the room.   Slide the lens back and forth between this screen and the object until a position is found where the picture of the netting appears on the screen as sharp as possible.

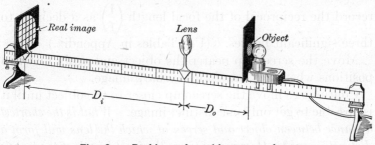

Fig. 58-2.   Real image formed by a convex lens.

Is the image larger or smaller than the object?

Cover one part of the object and *see if the image is erect or inverted.*

See whether the image is reversed from right to left.

Without moving the object or the screen, try to find another position of the lens that will give a sharp image. *Is it smaller or larger than the object, erect or inverted?*

When the image is smaller than the object, which is nearer the lens, the object or the image?

When the image is larger than the object, which is nearer the lens, the object or the image?

Record the position of the object and image and the two positions of the lens on the meter stick as accurately as possible.   Arrange your data and results in tabular form as shown on the following page:

POSITIONS			OBJECT-DISTANCE	IMAGE-DISTANCE	$\frac{1}{D_o} + \frac{1}{D_i}$	$\frac{1}{f}$
Object	Lens	Image				

Record the sum of the reciprocals of the object-distance $\left(\frac{1}{D_o}\right)$ and image-distance $\left(\frac{1}{D_i}\right)$ as a decimal fraction. Also record the reciprocal of the focal length $\left(\frac{1}{f}\right)$ as a decimal to three significant figures. (Use Tables in Appendix.)

Move the screen up nearer the object and again find two positions where the lens forms a sharp image.

Continue to move the screen up closer to the object until it is possible to get only one distinct image. *What is the shortest distance between object and screen at which the lens will form a distinct image? How many times the focal length of the lens is this minimum distance between object and image?*

Compare the sum of the reciprocals of the image- and object-distances with the reciprocal of the focal length as determined in Part I.

* * * *

Study of a photographic camera. Make a careful study of a photographic camera. What sort of lens is used? Is it a fixed-focus, rectilinear, or anastigmatic lens? If it has a combination lens, remove the front lens and focus the camera on a printed page. Is the image formed everywhere sharp? Replace the front lens and again focus on a printed page. What is the advantage of using a double lens? Why is the lens provided with a diaphragm having openings of various sizes ("stops")? How near can the camera be brought to an object and get a clear image?

What does one do if he wants a "close-up"? Make a photograph with the camera and record all the data, such as the name of the camera, focal length of lens, stop used, time of exposure, date, time of day, quality of light, and name of plate or film used. Paste a print of the picture in your notebook. Use an **exposure meter**.

EXPERIMENT 59

SIZE AND SHAPE OF A REAL IMAGE

I. *Is the real image of a straight line formed by a convex lens straight or curved? If it is curved, does its center bend toward or away from the lens?*

II. *How are the image-distance, object-distance, length of image, and length of object related?*

Strip of paper (about 20 × 75 cm.)	Pin
Meter stick	Hat pin
Double convex lens and holder	

Introduction. One important use of the double convex lens in optical instruments is to produce images which are larger than the objects. The ratio of the diameter (or length) of the image to the diameter of the object is the **magnifying power** of the lens. In this experiment we shall see that there is an important relation between the diameters of the object and of the image and their respective distances from the lens.

Directions. Lay a long strip of paper on the table so that the long side extends toward the window. Draw a line down the middle of the paper. Near the end farthest from the window, draw an arrow about 10 centimeters long. Divide the arrow into four equal parts and mark the points of division 1, 2, 3, 4, and 5 as shown in figure 59–1. On the long line (the axis), mark the position of the lens, which should be distant from point 3 of the arrow from one and a half to two times the focal length of the lens; that is, if the lens has a focal length of 12 centimeters, place it from 18 to 24 centimeters from the center of the arrow.

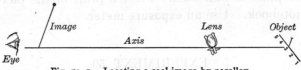

Fig. 59-1. Locating a real image by parallax.

Place the lens so that its center is directly over this point and its plane at right angles to the line. To locate the image-points corresponding to each of the five points of the object, stand a pin directly on point 3 and, using one eye only, look into the lens from the other end of the paper so as to see the image of the object pin. Move a hat pin until it just covers the image. To see the hat pin and image distinctly, the eye should be about 25 centimeters away from the pin. Move the hat pin toward and away from the lens until a position is found where, as the head moves slowly from side to side, the pin and the image keep exactly together, showing that each is at the same distance from the eye. This is called the **parallax method**. As soon as this position is sharply determined, mark a dot directly under the point of the hat pin and label it 3′.

Move the object pin along to 4 and locate in the same way the position of its image 4′. In this manner determine the position of the image of *each* of the five points of the object arrow. In locating these points, it is essential that the observer should not let any preconceived notion as to the proper position of the image points affect his judgment as to where each image point *really is*.

Construction. Connect the image points 1′ and 2′, 2′ and 3′, etc., with straight lines to get a rough idea of the shape of the whole image. Draw a straight line from each object point to its corresponding image point. *Where do these lines intersect?*

Connect the ends of the image arrow by a straight line, measure its length, and call it L_i. Measure the distance of the lens from the center of the object and the distance of the lens from the point where the straight line $(1'5')$ joining the ends of the image crosses the axis. Call these distances D_o and D_i respectively.

Call the length of the object L_o. *Compute the value of the ratio $\dfrac{L_i}{L_o}$, which is called the magnifying power of the lens.* Also *compute the value of the ratio $\dfrac{D_i}{D_o}$ and compare this result with the magnifying power.* (Express the ratio as a decimal fraction to three significant figures.)

Does the center of the image bend toward the lens or away from it?

To explain this curvature of the image, consider D_o for point 1 and D_o for point 3. Then, if the lens formula $\left(\dfrac{1}{D_o} + \dfrac{1}{D_i} = \dfrac{1}{f}\right)$ holds true and f is a constant for the lens, what would be expected of D_i for point 1 and D_i for point 3?

How is this defect in a lens corrected so as to give what the photographers call a "flat image"?

*　　*　　*　　*

Size and shape of a virtual image. Study the size and shape of a virtual image in the way just described for the real image. In this case, place the lens at or near the end of the median line and draw the object arrow (about 5 centimeters long) at a distance from the lens equal to about two-thirds its focal length. *How do you account for the shape of the virtual image? From your measurements, what relation do you find between the distances of object and image from the lens and their lengths?*

EXPERIMENT 60

COMPOUND MICROSCOPE AND TELESCOPE

I. *How may two convex lenses be arranged to act like a compound microscope?*

II. *How may two convex lenses be arranged to act like an astronomical telescope?*

Two short-focus lenses (f. 2.5–7.5 cm.)	Cardboard screen and holder
Two short-focus lenses (f. 2.5–7.5 cm.)	Two lens-holders
Long-focus lens (f. 25 cm.)	Screen with wire netting and
Meter stick and supports	holder

Electric lamp

Introduction. The great advances made in modern medicine are due more largely to the use of the compound microscope than to any other instrument. In recent years its use has been greatly extended, so that now the scientist studies even rocks and metals with the aid of the compound microscope.

Ever since the days when Galileo made his first telescope to study the stars, the astronomer has used larger and larger telescopes. But we all use a form of telescope every time we look through a field glass or an opera glass. The civil engineer uses a type of telescope in his transit and level. The big guns of both the army and the navy are equipped with telescopic sights.

In this experiment we shall see that both the compound microscope and the telescope consist essentially of two convex lenses mounted at either end of a suitable tube. The lens near the eye is called the **eyepiece**; the other lens is the **objective**. The objective forms a real image, and the eyepiece serves as a simple microscope to magnify this real image.

236

Directions. I. *Compound microscope*. Measure the focal length of each of two short-focus lenses, as in Experiment 58. Mount one of the lenses O on a meter stick with the lamp and its wire netting AB at one end, as shown in figure 60–1. Set up the cardboard screen S on the opposite side of the lens and move the lens back and forth until a distinct and enlarged image of the illuminated netting is seen

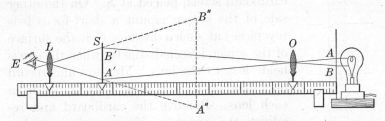

Fig. 60–1.   Model to illustrate a compound microscope.

on the cardboard. Mount the other lens L on the other side of the cardboard S at such a distance that the surface of the card is seen distinctly when the eye is held close to the lens. Measure and record on a diagram the distances between the screen and lenses. Now remove the cardboard (leaving its holder) and look through the lens L, holding the eye close up to the lens. If necessary, move the eyepiece lens back and forth slightly until you see clearly the inverted image of the illuminated netting. In this set-up, the lens L is used as a simple microscope to look at the real image formed by the objective lens at S. This combination of lenses represents a **compound microscope**.

Record the distance of the lamp netting from the objective lens. Compute the magnifying power of the objective from the ratio of the image-distance OS to the object-distance OA. Then compute the magnifying power of the eyepiece as the ratio $25/D_o$. Finally, *compute the magnifying power of the compound microscope by multiplying the magnifying power of the objective by the magnifying power of the eyepiece.*

II. *Astronomical telescope.* Find the focal length of the long-focus lens, as in Experiment 58. Mount it on the meter stick where the objective lens was located in the demonstration microscope. Then move this long-focus objective lens back and forth along the meter stick until a sharp image of

some distant object (such as the illuminated wire netting across the room) is formed on the cardboard screen placed at *S*. On the other side of the screen mount a short-focus lens (eyepiece) at such a distance that the surface of the screen is seen distinctly when the eye is held close to the lens. Measure and record on a diagram the distance of the screen from each lens. Remove the cardboard and readjust the eyepiece, if necessary, so that when you look through the eyepiece you see distinctly an enlarged, inverted image of the distant object. These two lenses thus arranged constitute the essential parts of a very crude astronomical telescope. Measure the distance between the lenses and compare this distance with the sum of the focal lengths.

Fig. 60–2. Object and image.

To measure the magnifying power of the telescope, fasten on the opposite wall of the room a strip of white paper with a series of thick black lines drawn across it at regular intervals of about one inch. Be sure that this paper scale is about on a level with the axis of the telescope and that the lenses are so adjusted as to give a sharp image. Then look through the telescope with one eye and at the same time look at the scale directly with the other eye. Adjust the telescope so that object and image appear about as shown in figure 60–2, and so that one mark of the image exactly coincides with one mark of the object. Count the number of spaces between two successive marks of the image. *This gives the magni-*

fying power of the telescope. Compare this value with the ratio of the focal length of the objective to the focal length of the eyepiece.

*   *   *   *

An experimental opera glass. With a long-focus (40 cm.) double convex lens as an objective and with a concave lens as an eyepiece, set up a demonstration model of the **opera glass,** or Galilean telescope. Make the distance between the eyepiece and objective equal to the difference between the focal lengths of the two lenses.* Use a cardboard diaphragm with a quarter-inch aperture mounted between the lenses near the eyepiece. *Is the image erect or inverted? How much is it magnified?* Measure the magnifying power of the model opera glass and compare the result with the ratio of the focal lengths of the objective and eyepiece.

* To measure the focal length of a concave lens, allow the sunlight to fall upon the lens, over which is a diaphragm. Receive the emergent light upon a screen at such a distance that the illuminated spot has twice the dimensions of the aperture in the diaphragm. Then the distance between the lens and the screen is the required focal length. Why?

EXPERIMENT 61

WAVE LENGTH OF LIGHT

I. *What is the wave length of sodium light as measured by a diffraction grating?*

II. *What is the wave length of lithium light?*

Replica of grating with 14,438 lines per inch
Two meter sticks mounted at right angles
Holder for grating
Bunsen burner
Asbestos paper
Solutions of sodium chloride and lithium chloride
Screen with slit

Introduction. When a beam of light passes through a narrow opening, there is a spreading of light and interference, which is called *diffraction*. If a plate of glass has many equally spaced parallel lines ruled on its surface, it is found

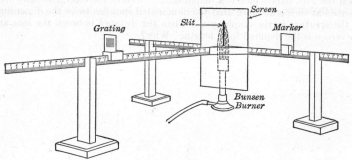

Fig. 61-1. Measuring the wave-length of light with a grating.

that such a *grating* will transmit light through the unruled spaces in the glass but will diffuse the light falling on the ruled lines. These lines are ruled so close together that there are several thousand per inch. The average width of one line and one space is called the *grating space*. If one places his eye close to such a *transparent diffraction grating* and looks through it at a narrow slit in an opaque screen which is placed before a sodium flame, he sees besides the slit straight ahead, several images of the slit on each side (Fig. 61–1). These images are more plainly visible if the room is darkened. The image nearest the slit, on either side of it, is called the bright-line spectrum of the *first order*, and the image next in position, on either side, the spectrum of *second order*, and so on.

It can be proved that the wave length (λ) of the particular color of light used is equal to the grating space (d) multiplied by the sine of the angle (α), which is the angle between the image of the slit seen directly and the diffracted image.* That is,

$$\lambda = d \sin \alpha$$

and for the second-order spectra

$$\lambda = \frac{d \sin \alpha}{2}.$$

Directions. Arrange the apparatus as in the diagram (Fig. 61–2), which shows the eye, the grating, the slit in the opaque screen, the Bunsen burner, the first-order images S_1 and S_2, and the second-order images S_1' and S_2'. Place the two meter sticks at right angles, as shown, and set the slit so that it is opposite the midpoint of one stick. Soak a strip of asbestos paper in salt (sodium chloride) solution and attach it to the Bunsen burner so that it will give a steady sodium

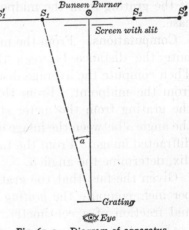

Fig. 61–2.   Diagram of apparatus.

* For more details and the proof see BLACK's *Introductory Course in College Physics*, p. 665.

flame. Be sure to keep the air holes open at the base of the burner.*

The instructor in charge of the laboratory will place the grating in the holder on the meter stick.

CAUTION. *Do not touch these gratings with anything!*

Darken the room and look through the grating at the slit. Then turn the eye slightly and observe the image on the left side. To locate the position of this image as precisely as possible, let your co-worker move a cardboard marker along the meter stick until the edge of the cardboard seems to coincide with the image. † Then read and record its position S_1 on the meter stick. Repeat this operation several times and each time record the position. Finally compute the mean value for S_1.

Repeat this operation with the image on the right side and locate the position of S_2.

Then move the grating nearer the slit so that the images of the second order can be located on the meter stick at S_1' and S_2'. Repeat the experiment. Record the distance of the grating from the midpoint of the meter stick in each case.

Computations. From the mean positions S_1 and S_2, compute the distance between these two first-order images. Then compute the average distance of this first-order image from the midpoint. From this value and the distance of the grating from the meter stick, compute the tangent of the angle α between the image of the slit seen directly and the diffracted image. From the table of tangents in the Appendix, determine the angle α.

Given the fact that the grating is ruled with 14,438 lines per inch, compute the *grating space d* expressed as a decimal fraction of a centimeter. Finally, compute the wave

---

* A more convenient source of light for this experiment is a *mercury-vapor lamp* for laboratory purposes.

† It adds to the precision of this experiment if a vertical line is ruled in ink on the back side of the grating glass.

length, expressed in centimeters, for sodium light from the equation

$$\lambda = d \sin \alpha.$$

Then carry through a similar calculation, using the data for the second-order spectra.

Compute your percentage error in this experiment, assuming the average wave length of sodium lines to be 0.0000589 centimeter.

If time permits, repeat the experiment, using lithium salt. Determine the wave length of the lithium lines.

Tabulate the data obtained, arranging your calculations in an orderly fashion.

Questions. When a source of red light is used, do the images of the slit appear to be nearer to or farther from the slit than when the yellow light was employed? Why?

MODERN PHYSICS

BLOCK IX. RADIO AND RADIUM

Suggestive Questions

1. Why did Roentgen's discovery start a new epoch in physics?
2. Why are men producing artificial lightning?
3. Why has the neon tube become so popular for display purposes?
4. Why is Sir J. J. Thomson sometimes called the father of the electron?
5. Does a vacuum tube in a radio receiving set increase the electric current?
6. Why should a dentist use X-ray photographs?
7. What is the difference between an atom and an ion?
8. Why is the filament in a vacuum tube sometimes called the heater?
9. Why is the plate in a vacuum tube always charged positively?
10. What is the function of the vacuum tube used in long-distance telephony?
11. If air is usually an insulator, how can it be made a conductor?
12. How can a vacuum tube be used to rectify an alternating current?
13. Why should distant electrical storms interfere with local radio sets?
14. Why should a hot filament furnish more electrons than a cold filament?
15. Why should a partially evacuated tube conduct electricity better than a tube filled with air under normal pressure?

EXPERIMENT 62

CHARACTERISTICS OF A VACUUM TUBE

What is the relation between the plate current and the grid voltage of a vacuum tube?

Radio amplifying tube (such as 6J5G) and octal base socket

Filament rheostat (10 ohms)

Voltmeter for heater filament

Milliammeter for plate circuit (0 − 5) such as Weston 301

Grid battery C (12 volts, dry cells)

Plate battery B (45 volts, dry cells)

Heater battery A (6-volt storage)

Voltmeter (0 − 30 volts)

Rheostat to be used as a potentiometer

Two-pole double-throw switch

Introduction. The vacuum tube has made possible many important advances in radio communication. It not only serves as a detector of radio oscillations but is also used to generate, to amplify, and to modulate these same oscillations. It has found many applications in other fields of electrical engineering, such as in ordinary telephony with wires, where its use has made possible conversations over great distances (3000 miles).

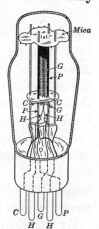

Fig. 62–1. Heater-cathode type of vacuum tube.

The form of the tube is being rapidly improved. But the operation of this tube, of whatever form and for whatever use, depends on the properties of very minute particles of negative electricity, called **electrons**. A common form of amplifier tube contains the **filament**, a **cathode**, a **plate**, and a **grid** (Fig. 62–1). It is called a *heater-cathode* type of vacuum tube. In this type of tube the heater loop H is placed along the axis of the tube and the cathode C

is a metal sleeve coated with active material. The hot cathode shoots off electrons. If the plate is positively charged, there is a passing of electrons to the plate which is equivalent to the flow of current *from* the plate *to* the cathode, according to the usual idea of the flow of an electric

Fig. 62-2. Testing a heater-type of radio tube.

current from the positive to the negative potential. Carefully note this distinction between the direction of *electron flow* and of *electric current*. Nevertheless, remember that the magnitude of the current flowing through the tube from the plate is determined by the number of electrons that travel across the tube and reach the plate per second.

If we increase the heater current, we thereby increase the cathode temperature, which means that more electrons are shot off. If we increase the plate voltage, we also increase the number of electrons reaching the plate every second, which means that we increase the plate current.

By introducing the **grid** between the cathode and the plate, we have another most effective means of controlling the plate current. By making the potential of the grid *positive* or *negative* as regards the cathode, it is possible to hasten or obstruct the flow of electrons and thus to vary the plate current.

In this experiment we shall study the relation between the *grid potential* and the *plate current*. As a result of our measurements, we shall be able to plot a characteristic curve to show graphically this relationship, because it is upon such a curve that the most commonly accepted explanation of the tube's operation is based. This is only one of several characteristic curves which are used to study the relationship

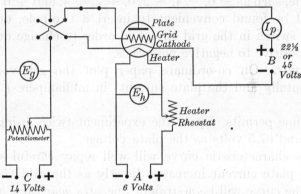

Fig 62–2. Connections for measuring the plate current with various grid potentials.

between the several factors — plate potential, plate current, grid potential, grid current, and heater current. Two variable factors having been selected, the other three must remain fixed.

Directions. *Connections.* The apparatus should be connected up as in figure 62–2. It will be seen that besides the "A" battery in the heater circuit and the "B" battery in the plate circuit, we have a third battery in the grid circuit. It will also be noted that a rheostat is placed across the grid battery C, to serve as a potentiometer, and also a reversing switch so that we may quickly get various positive and negative grid potentials. The milliammeter (I_p) in the plate circuit measures the *plate current*, and the voltmeter (E_g) measures the *grid voltage*. The heater current is kept constant by a filament rheostat and voltmeter, and the plate voltage is also kept constant by means of a "*B*" battery.

First adjust the heater rheostat until the heater voltage, as indicated by the voltmeter E_h, is normal; that is, whatever is specified by the makers of the tube as normal. Then make the plate voltage 45 volts. Now measure the plate current for several potentials of the grid referred to the cathode, such as − 6, − 4, − 2, 0, + 2, + 4, and + 6 volts. It will be found convenient to insert a two-pole, double-throw switch in the grid circuit in order to change quickly from positive to negative potentials.

Results. On co-ordinate paper plot the grid voltages horizontally and the plate current (in milliamperes) vertically.

If time permits, repeat the experiment twice, using 22.5 volts and 67.5 volts as the plate voltage.

This characteristic curve will well repay careful study. If the plate current increases directly as the grid voltage, then the curve will be a straight line. *Is your curve or any part of it approximately a straight line? What does it mean?* If the plate current increases more rapidly over one certain range than over another (for a given change in grid potential), then the curve will be steeper over that range. *What part of your curve is steepest? What does this indicate?* If the tube reaches a saturation point where an increase in grid potential produces almost no increase in the plate current, the curve will flatten out into a horizontal line at the upper extremity. *Have you reached the saturation point?*

In using such a tube as an amplifier, it is desirable to arrange the conditions so that a change in grid voltage will produce a proportional change in plate current. *What grid potential would you suggest as desirable for your tube? Why?*

APPENDIX

I. Rules for Computation

$$\text{Area of triangle} = \frac{\text{base} \times \text{altitude}}{2}$$

$$\text{Circumference of circle} = \pi D$$

$$\text{Area of circle} = \pi R^2 = 0.785\, D^2$$

$$\text{Surface of sphere} = 4\,\pi R^2 = \pi D^2$$

$$\text{Volume of sphere} = \frac{4\,\pi R^3}{3} = 0.524\, D^3$$

$$\left.\begin{array}{l}\text{Volume of prism} \\ \text{Volume of cylinder}\end{array}\right\} = \text{area of base} \times \text{altitude}$$

$$\pi = 3\tfrac{1}{7},\ \text{or } 3.14$$

II. Table of Equivalents

1 centimeter = 0.394 inch	1 inch = 2.54 centimeters
1 kilometer = 0.621 mile	1 foot = 30.5 centimeters
1 kilogram = 2.20 pounds	1 ounce = 28.4 grams
1 liter = 1.06 quarts	1 pound = 454 grams
1 cm.³ water weighs 1 gram	1 ft.³ water weighs 62.4 pounds

III. Table of Densities

(In grams per cubic centimeter)

Alcohol, 95%	0.807	Magnesium	1.74
Aluminum	2.70	Marble	2.5–2.8
Brass	8.4	Mercury	13.6
Carbon tetrachloride	1.60	Milk	1.03
Coal (anthracite)	1.4–1.8	Nickel	8.9
Copper	8.93	Paraffin	0.824–0.94
Gasoline	0.75	Platinum	21.5
Glass (flint)	3.0–3.6	Sea water	1.03
Glass (crown)	2.4–2.7	Silver	10.5
Gold	19.3	Tin	7.3
Ice	0.917	Wood — Ebony	1.2
Iron	7.1–7.9	Oak	0.7–0.9
Lead	11.4	Pine	0.4–0.6
Lignum vitae	1.33	Zinc	7.1

IV. Density of Dry Air at Different Temperatures and Pressures (Grams per Liter)

Temp.	Pressure in Millimeters							
	710	720	730	740	750	760	770	780
0° C.	1.208	1.225	1.242	1.259	1.276	1.293	1.310	1.327
2	1.199	1.216	1.233	1.250	1.267	1.284	1.300	1.317
4	1.190	1.207	1.224	1.241	1.258	1.274	1.291	1.308
6	1.182	1.199	1.215	1.232	1.248	1.265	1.282	1.298
8	1.173	1.190	1.207	1.223	1.240	1.256	1.273	1.289
10	1.165	1.182	1.198	1.214	1.231	1.247	1.264	1.280
12	1.157	1.173	1.190	1.206	1.222	1.238	1.255	1.271
14	1.149	1.165	1.181	1.197	1.214	1.230	1.246	1.262
16	1.141	1.157	1.173	1.189	1.205	1.221	1.237	1.253
18	1.133	1.149	1.165	1.181	1.197	1.213	1.229	1.245
20	1.125	1.141	1.157	1.173	1.189	1.205	1.220	1.236
22	1.118	1.133	1.149	1.165	1.181	1.196	1.212	1.228
24	1.110	1.126	1.141	1.157	1.173	1.188	1.204	1.220
26	1.103	1.118	1.134	1.149	1.165	1.180	1.196	1.211
28	1.095	1.111	1.126	1.142	1.157	1.173	1.188	1.203
30	1.088	1.103	1.119	1.134	1.149	1.165	1.180	1.195

V. Tensile Strength of Wires *

Material	Kilograms per Square Milli- meter	Material	Kilograms per Square Milli- meter
Aluminum, rolled . .	17–20	Nickel	53
Brass wire	31–39	Platinum	33
Bronze, phosphor . .	69–108	Steel	about 110
Copper, hard-drawn .	40–46	Steel, crucible . . .	186–233
Iron, ordinary . . .	about 46	Zinc	11–15

* From Kaye and Laby, *Physical and Chemical Constants*, Longmans, Green and Co.

VI. COEFFICIENT OF LINEAR EXPANSION OF SOLIDS

(Centigrade Scale)

Aluminum	0.0000231	"Invar" (Nickel steel) . 0.0000009
Brass	0.0000189	Quartz (fused) 0.0000005
Copper	0.0000167	Steel 0.000011
Glass (soft)	0.0000085	Zinc 0.000029

VII. SPECIFIC HEAT OF VARIOUS SUBSTANCES

Solids

Aluminum	0.219	Lead	0.0305
Brass	0.090	Nickel	0.109
Copper	0.0936	Platinum	0.0324
Glass	0.190	Silver	0.056
Ice	0.502	Tin	0.055
Iron	0.119	Zinc	0.094

Liquids

Alcohol, ethyl at 17° C. . .	0.602	Kerosene	0.5–0.6
Carbon disulfide at 15° C. .	0.230	Mercury at 20° C. . . .	0.0333
Glycerin, 0°–100° C. . . .	0.576	Water	1.000

VIII. WEIGHT OF WATER VAPOR IN SATURATED AIR

TEMPERATURE ° F.	WEIGHT IN GRAINS * PER CUBIC FOOT	TEMPERATURE ° C.	WEIGHT IN GRAMS PER CUBIC METER
− 20°	0.21	− 30°	0.44
0	0.54	− 20	1.04
+ 20	1.30	− 10	2.28
40	2.86	0	4.87
50	4.09	+ 10	9.36
60	5.76	20	17.15
70	7.99	30	30.08
80	10.95	+ 40	50.67

* One pound (Avoirdupois) is equal to 7000 grains.

IX. Relative Humidity, Per Cent

Dry-bulb Thermometer ° F.	Difference between Dry- and Wet-bulb Thermometers												
	5.0°	6.0°	7.0°	8.0°	9.0°	10.0°	11.0°	12.0°	13.0°	14.0°	15.0°	16.0°	17.0°
60°	73	68	63	58	53	48	44	39	34	30	26	22	18
61°	73	68	63	58	54	49	44	40	35	32	27	23	19
62°	74	69	64	59	54	50	45	41	37	32	28	24	20
63°	74	69	64	60	55	50	46	42	37	33	29	25	21
64°	74	70	65	60	56	51	47	43	38	34	30	26	22
65°	75	70	66	61	56	52	48	44	39	35	31	27	24
66°	75	71	66	61	57	53	48	44	40	36	32	29	25
67°	75	71	66	62	58	53	49	45	41	37	33	30	26
68°	76	71	67	62	58	54	50	46	42	38	34	31	27
69°	76	72	67	63	59	55	51	47	43	39	35	32	28
70°	77	72	68	64	59	55	51	48	44	40	36	33	29
71°	77	72	68	64	60	56	52	48	45	41	37	33	30
72°	77	73	69	65	61	57	53	49	45	42	38	34	31
73°	78	73	69	65	61	57	53	50	46	42	39	35	32
74°	78	74	70	66	62	58	54	50	47	43	40	36	33
75°	78	74	70	66	62	58	54	51	47	44	40	37	34
76°	78	74	70	66	62	59	55	51	48	44	41	38	34
77°	79	74	71	67	63	59	56	52	48	45	42	39	35
78°	79	75	71	67	63	60	56	53	49	46	43	39	36
79°	79	75	71	68	64	60	57	53	50	46	43	40	37

This table is calculated for rapid forced ventilation.

X. Resistance of Annealed Copper Wire

B. & S. Gauge	Diameter in Millimeters	Diameter in Mils	Area in Circular Mils	Ohms per 1000 Ft. at 20° C.	Feet per Lb. Double Cotton Covered
10	2.59	101.9	10,381.	1.00	30.9
11	2.31	90.7	8,234.	1.26	38.9
12	2.05	80.8	6,530.	1.59	48.8
13	1.83	72.0	5,178.	2.00	61.5
14	1.63	64.1	4,107.	2.52	77.4
15	1.45	57.1	3,257.	3.18	97.2
16	1.29	50.8	2,583.	4.01	122.
17	1.15	45.3	2,048.	5.06	153.
18	1.02	40.3	1,624.	6.37	192.
19	.90	35.9	1,288.	8.04	247.
20	.81	32.0	1,022.	10.1	298.
21	.72	28.5	810.	12.8	375.
22	.64	25.3	642.	16.1	472.
23	.57	22.6	509.	20.3	585.
24	.51	20.1	404.	25.6	730.
25	.46	17.90	320.	32.3	901.
26	.41	15.94	254.	40.8	1123.
27	.36	14.20	202.	51.4	1389.
28	.32	12.64	159.8	64.8	1695.
29	.29	11.26	126.7	81.7	2127.
30	.26	10.02	100.5	103.	2564.
31	.23	8.93	79.7	130.	
32	.20	7.95	63.2	164.	
33	.18	7.08	50.1	207.	
34	.16	6.30	39.7	261.	
35	.14	5.61	31.5	328.	
36	.13	5.00	25.0	414.	
37	.11	4.45	19.8	522.	
38	.10	3.97	15.7	659.	
39	.09	3.53	12.5	830.	
40	.08	3.15	9.9	1047.	

It will be noticed in the table above that #13 wire is about half the size of #10 wire and so has twice as much resistance. In the same way #16 wire is half the size of #13 and has double the resistance.

XI. Density of Hydrogen (in Grams per Liter), Measured over Water, at Varying Temperatures and Pressures

(To get weight of 1 cc., move decimal point 3 places to left.)

Pressure (mm.)	Temperature in Degrees Centigrade									
	15°	16°	17°	18°	19°	20°	21°	22°	23°	24°
740	0.0815	0.0811	0.0807	0.0803	0.0799	0.0795	0.0792	0.0787	0.0784	0.0780
741	.0816	.0812	.0808	.0804	.0800	.0797	.0793	.0788	.0785	.0781
742	.0817	.0813	.0809	.0805	.0801	.0798	.0794	.0789	.0786	.0782
743	.0818	.0814	.0810	.0806	.0803	.0799	.0795	.0790	.0787	.0783
744	.0819	.0815	.0812	.0808	.0804	.0800	.0796	.0792	.0788	.0784
745	.0820	.0817	.0813	.0809	.0805	.0801	.0797	.0793	.0789	.0785
746	.0821	.0818	.0814	.0810	.0806	.0802	.0798	.0794	.0790	.0786
747	.0823	.0819	.0815	.0811	.0807	.0803	.0799	.0795	.0791	.0787
748	.0824	.0820	.0816	.0812	.0808	.0804	.0800	.0796	.0792	.0788
749	.0825	.0821	.0817	.0813	.0809	.0806	.0802	.0797	.0793	.0789
750	.0826	.0822	.0818	.0814	.0810	.0807	.0803	.0798	.0795	.0791
751	.0827	.0823	.0819	.0815	.0811	.0808	.0804	.0799	.0796	.0792
752	.0828	.0824	.0820	.0816	.0813	.0809	.0805	.0800	.0797	.0793
753	.0829	.0826	.0822	.0818	.0814	.0810	.0806	.0802	.0798	.0794
754	.0830	.0827	.0823	.0819	.0815	.0811	.0807	.0803	.0799	.0795
755	.0832	.0828	.0824	.0820	.0816	.0812	.0808	.0804	.0800	.0796
756	.0833	.0829	.0825	.0821	.0817	.0813	.0809	.0805	.0801	.0797
757	.0834	.0830	.0826	.0822	.0818	.0814	.0810	.0806	.0802	.0798
758	.0835	.0831	.0827	.0823	.0819	.0815	.0812	.0807	.0803	.0799
759	.0836	.0832	.0828	.0824	.0820	.0817	.0813	.0808	.0804	.0800
760	.0837	.0833	.0829	.0825	.0822	.0818	.0814	.0809	.0806	.0802
761	.0838	.0835	.0831	.0826	.0823	.0819	.0815	.0810	.0807	.0803
762	.0839	.0836	.0832	.0828	.0824	.0820	.0816	.0812	.0808	.0804
763	.0841	.0837	.0833	.0829	.0825	.0821	.0817	.0813	.0809	.0805
764	.0842	.0838	.0834	.0830	.0826	.0822	.0818	.0814	.0810	.0806
765	.0843	.0839	.0835	.0831	.0827	.0823	.0819	.0815	.0811	.0807
766	.0844	.0840	.0836	.0832	.0828	.0824	.0820	.0816	.0812	.0808
767	.0845	.0841	.0837	.0833	.0829	.0825	.0822	.0817	.0813	.0809
768	.0846	.0842	.0838	.0834	.0830	.0826	.0823	.0818	.0814	.0810
769	.0847	.0844	.0840	.0835	.0832	.0828	.0824	.0819	.0815	.0812

SINE AND TANGENT OF AN ANGLE

Let BAC (Fig. A–1) be any given angle.   From *any* point B on one side of the angle draw a perpendicular BC to the other side, thus forming the right-angled triangle ABC.   Suppose we measure the hypotenuse AB and find it to be 10.00 centimeters and the opposite side BC and find it to be 5.05 centimeters. Then the ratio of the opposite side to the hypotenuse is $\dfrac{BC}{AB} = \dfrac{5.05}{10.00} = 0.505$.

We might choose any other point on AB but in any case we should obtain the same value for the ratio of the *opposite side* to the *hypotenuse* so long as we used the same angle BAC.

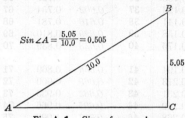

$$Sin \angle A = \frac{5.05}{10.0} = 0.505$$

10.0   5.05

Fig. A–1.   Sine of an angle.

In the same way we might measure the *opposite side* BC and the *adjacent side* AC.   We should find that the ratio of the opposite side to the adjacent side $\dfrac{BC}{AC}$ is constant for any given angle.

In mathematics these constant ratios have been given distinguishing names.

The ratio $\dfrac{BC}{AB}$ is called the ***sine*** of the angle BAC.

The ratio $\dfrac{BC}{AC}$ is called the ***tangent*** of the angle BAC.

The values of these ratios have been calculated for all angles and are given in trigonometric tables.   These ratios, with the values carried out to three decimals, will be found on page 256.   They are called the ***natural sines*** and ***natural tangents*** to distinguish them from the logarithmic sines and tangents.

It will be helpful to remember that the tangent of an angle of 45° is 1 since in this case BC is equal to AC.   For angles less than 45°, the tangent is less than 1 and for angles between 45° and 90° it is more than 1, being infinity at 90°.   It is also obvious that no angle can have a sine greater than 1.

XII. Natural Sines and Tangents

Angle	Sine	Tangent	Angle	Sine	Tangent	Angle	Sine	Tangent
0°	0.000	0.000						
1	0.017	0.017	31°	0.515	0.601	61°	0.875	1.804
2	0.035	0.035	32	0.530	0.625	62	0.883	1.881
3	0.052	0.052	33	0.545	0.649	63	0.891	1.963
4	0.070	0.070	34	0.559	0.675	64	0.899	2.050
5	0.087	0.087	35	0.574	0.700	65	0.906	2.145
6	0.105	0.105	36	0.588	0.727	66	0.914	2.246
7	0.122	0.123	37	0.602	0.754	67	0.921	2.356
8	0.139	0.141	38	0.616	0.781	68	0.927	2.475
9	0.156	0.158	39	0.629	0.810	69	0.934	2.605
10	0.174	0.176	40	0.643	0.839	70	0.940	2.747
11	0.191	0.194	41	0.656	0.869	71	0.946	2.904
12	0.208	0.213	42	0.669	0.900	72	0.951	3.078
13	0.225	0.231	43	0.682	0.933	73	0.956	3.271
14	0.242	0.249	44	0.695	0.966	74	0.961	3.487
15	0.259	0.268	45	0.707	1.000	75	0.966	3.732
16	0.276	0.287	46	0.719	1.036	76	0.970	4.011
17	0.292	0.306	47	0.731	1.072	77	0.974	4.331
18	0.309	0.325	48	0.743	1.111	78	0.978	4.705
19	0.326	0.344	49	0.755	1.150	79	0.982	5.145
20	0.342	0.364	50	0.766	1.192	80	0.985	5.671
21	0.358	0.384	51	0.777	1.235	81	0.988	6.314
22	0.375	0.404	52	0.788	1.280	82	0.990	7.115
23	0.391	0.424	53	0.799	1.327	83	0.993	8.144
24	0.407	0.445	54	0.809	1.376	84	0.995	9.514
25	0.423	0.466	55	0.819	1.428	85	0.996	11.43
26	0.438	0.488	56	0.829	1.483	86	0.998	14.30
27	0.454	0.510	57	0.839	1.540	87	0.999	19.08
28	0.469	0.532	58	0.848	1.600	88	0.999	28.64
29	0.485	0.554	59	0.857	1.664	89	1.000	57.29
30	0.500	0.577	60	0.866	1.732	90	1.000	Infinity

HINTS ABOUT PLOTTING CURVES

In scientific work we frequently have a result which changes according to some variable factor and we wish to show graphically just how the result depends upon this factor.

For example, suppose we find that a certain liquid cools as shown by the following data:

Time	2 min.	6	8	13	18	24	32	38	44	49
Temp.	73° C.	64	58	51	45	38	32	27	23	21

On a sheet of co-ordinate paper which is ruled in squares, we select a certain horizontal line near the bottom as the *time* axis and a certain vertical line to the left as the *temperature* axis; the intersection of the two lines (in the lower left-hand corner) is called the *origin*. In this case we shall find it convenient to let each horizontal space represent 5 minutes and each vertical space 10°. Each observation given in our table is then plotted as shown in figure A–2.

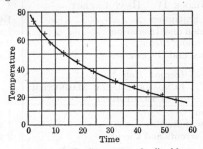

Fig. A–2. Cooling curve of a liquid.

The origin represents the beginning of the experiment, 2 minutes is represented by 0.4 of the first space to the right, and 73° is 0.3 of a space above the 70° line and directly over the proper time space. At this point we make a dot and then make it conspicuous by drawing through it fine crosslines or, better still, by drawing a tiny circle around the point. In the same way the other points are plotted and a curve is drawn through the resulting points. It will be noted that it was not possible to draw a smooth curve through all the points, so we assume that those points not exactly on the curve are probably somewhat in error.

It requires some experience to choose the proper scale for two sets of variables, but it is evident that the two scales need not be alike. It is desirable to choose such a scale that the points cover a large part of the sheet of paper in both directions. Often it is more convenient to have the origin not represent the zero value on each scale but some round number just under the minimum value. The quantity represented by each scale must be plainly indicated and also the units used.

CHAPTER	SUBJECT	TIME	EXPERIMENTS
	(First Half Year)		
	BLOCK I. MEASUREMENT. SIMPLE MACHINE ELEMENTS		
1	Introduction: Weights and Measures . . .	1 week	1 and 2
2	Simple Machines: Levers and Pulleys . . .	2 weeks	3 to 5
3	Work, Power, and Efficiency	2 weeks	6 to 9
	BLOCK II. MECHANICS OF FLUIDS		
4	Mechanics of Liquids	2 weeks	10 to 12
5	Mechanics of Gases	2 weeks	13 to 15
6	Properties of Matter	1 week	16 and 17
	BLOCK III. FORCES AND MOTIONS		
7	Forces Acting through a Point	1 week	18 and 19
8	Accelerated Motion	1 week	20 and 21
9	Three Laws of Motion	1 week	22 and 23
10	Potential and Kinetic Energy	1 week	24
	BLOCK IV. HEAT ENERGY		
11	Heat and Expansion	1 week	25 to 27
12	Transmission and Insulation	1 week	
13	Ice, Water, and Steam	2 weeks	28 to 32
14	Steam, Gas, and Oil Engines	1 week	33 and 34
	(Second Half Year)		
	BLOCK V. FUNDAMENTALS OF MAGNETISM AND ELECTRICITY		
15	Magnetism	1 week	35
16	Electricity at Rest	1 week	
17	Electric Currents and Circuits	2 weeks	36 to 41
	BLOCK VI. EFFECTS OF ELECTRIC CURRENTS		
18	Effects of Electric Currents	2 weeks	42 to 45
19	Generators and Motors	1 week	46 and 47
20	Alternating Currents	2 weeks	48 and 49
	BLOCK VII. SOUND WAVES AND MUSIC		
21	Sound Waves	1 week	50 and 51
22	Musical Sounds	1 week	52
	BLOCK VIII. LIGHT WAVES AND THEIR USES		
23	Lamps and Reflectors	2 weeks	53 to 56
24	Lenses and Optical Instruments	3 weeks	57 to 60
25	Spectra and Color	1 week	61
	BLOCK IX. RADIO AND RADIUM		
26	Vacuum Tubes and Radium	1 week	62
27	Radio Communication	1 week	
	Total	38 weeks	

N	0	1	2	3	4	5	6	7	8	9	Subtract Differences								
											1	2	3	4	5	6	7	8	9
10	1000	9901	9804	9709	9615	9524	9434	9346	9259	9174	9	18	27	36	45	55	64	73	82
11	9091	9009	8929	8850	8772	8696	8621	8547	8475	8403	8	15	23	30	38	45	53	61	68
12	8333	8264	8197	8130	8065	8000	7937	7874	7813	7752	6	13	19	26	32	38	45	51	58
13	7692	7634	7576	7519	7463	7407	7353	7299	7246	7194	5	11	16	22	27	33	38	44	49
14	7143	7092	7042	6993	6944	6897	6849	6803	6757	6711	5	10	14	19	24	29	33	38	43
15	6667	6623	6579	6536	6494	6452	6410	6369	6329	6289	4	8	13	17	21	25	29	33	38
16	6250	6211	6173	6135	6098	6061	6024	5988	5952	5917	4	7	11	15	18	22	26	29	33
17	5882	5848	5814	5780	5747	5714	5682	5650	5618	5587	3	6	10	13	16	20	23	26	29
18	5556	5525	5495	5464	5435	5405	5376	5348	5319	5291	3	6	9	12	15	17	20	23	26
19	5263	5236	5208	5181	5155	5128	5102	5076	5051	5025	3	5	8	11	13	16	18	21	24
20	5000	4975	4950	4926	4902	4878	4854	4831	4808	4785	2	5	7	10	12	14	17	19	21
21	4762	4739	4717	4695	4673	4651	4630	4608	4587	4566	2	4	7	9	11	13	15	17	19
22	4545	4525	4505	4484	4464	4444	4425	4405	4386	4367	2	4	6	8	10	12	14	16	18
23	4348	4329	4310	4292	4274	4255	4237	4219	4202	4184	2	4	5	7	9	11	13	14	16
24	4167	4149	4132	4115	4098	4082	4065	4049	4032	4016	2	3	5	7	8	10	12	13	15
25	4000	3984	3968	3953	3937	3922	3906	3891	3876	3861	2	3	5	6	8	9	11	12	14
26	3846	3831	3817	3802	3788	3774	3759	3745	3731	3717	1	3	4	6	7	8	10	11	13
27	3704	3690	3676	3663	3650	3636	3623	3610	3597	3584	1	3	4	5	7	8	9	11	12
28	3571	3559	3546	3534	3521	3509	3497	3484	3472	3460	1	2	4	5	6	7	9	10	11
29	3448	3436	3425	3413	3401	3390	3378	3367	3356	3344	1	2	3	5	6	7	8	9	10
30	3333	3322	3311	3300	3289	3279	3268	3257	3247	3236	1	2	3	4	5	6	7	9	10
31	3226	3215	3205	3195	3185	3175	3165	3155	3145	3135	1	2	3	4	5	6	7	8	9
32	3125	3115	3106	3096	3086	3077	3067	3058	3049	3040	1	2	3	4	5	6	7	8	9
33	3030	3021	3012	3003	2994	2985	2976	2967	2959	2950	1	2	3	4	4	5	6	7	8
34	2941	2933	2924	2915	2907	2899	2890	2882	2874	2865	1	2	3	3	4	5	6	7	8
35	2857	2849	2841	2833	2825	2817	2809	2801	2793	2786	1	2	2	3	4	5	6	6	7
36	2778	2770	2762	2755	2747	2740	2732	2725	2717	2710	1	2	2	3	4	5	5	6	7
37	2703	2695	2688	2681	2674	2667	2660	2653	2646	2639	1	1	2	3	4	4	5	6	6
38	2632	2625	2618	2611	2604	2597	2591	2584	2577	2571	1	1	2	3	3	4	5	5	6
39	2564	2558	2551	2545	2538	2532	2525	2519	2513	2506	1	1	2	3	3	4	4	5	6
40	2500	2494	2488	2481	2475	2469	2463	2457	2451	2445	1	1	2	2	3	4	4	5	5
41	2439	2433	2427	2421	2415	2410	2404	2398	2392	2387	1	1	2	2	3	3	4	4	5
42	2381	2375	2370	2364	2358	2353	2347	2342	2336	2331	1	1	2	2	3	3	4	4	5
43	2326	2320	2315	2309	2304	2299	2294	2288	2283	2278	1	1	2	2	3	3	4	4	5
44	2273	2268	2262	2257	2252	2247	2242	2237	2232	2227	1	1	2	2	3	3	4	4	5
45	2222	2217	2212	2208	2203	2198	2193	2188	2183	2179	0	1	1	2	2	3	3	4	4
46	2174	2169	2165	2160	2155	2151	2146	2141	2137	2132	0	1	1	2	2	3	3	4	4
47	2128	2123	2119	2114	2110	2105	2101	2096	2092	2088	0	1	1	2	2	3	3	4	4
48	2083	2079	2075	2070	2066	2062	2058	2053	2049	2045	0	1	1	2	2	3	3	3	4
49	2041	2037	2033	2028	2024	2020	2016	2012	2008	2004	0	1	1	2	2	2	3	3	4
50	2000	1996	1992	1988	1984	1980	1976	1972	1969	1965	0	1	1	2	2	2	3	3	4
51	1961	1957	1953	1949	1946	1942	1938	1934	1931	1927	0	1	1	2	2	2	3	3	3
52	1923	1919	1916	1912	1908	1905	1901	1898	1894	1890	0	1	1	1	2	2	3	3	3
53	1887	1883	1880	1876	1873	1869	1866	1862	1859	1855	0	1	1	1	2	2	2	3	3
54	1852	1848	1845	1842	1838	1835	1832	1828	1825	1821	0	1	1	1	2	2	2	3	3
	0	1	2	3	4	5	6	7	8	9	1	2	3	4	5	6	7	8	9
											Subtract Differences								

N	0	1	2	3	4	5	6	7	8	9	Subtract Differences								
											1	2	3	4	5	6	7	8	9
55	1818	1815	1812	1808	1805	1802	1799	1795	1792	1789	0	1	1	1	2	2	2	3	3
56	1786	1783	1779	1776	1773	1770	1767	1764	1761	1757	0	1	1	1	2	2	2	3	3
57	1754	1751	1748	1745	1742	1739	1736	1733	1730	1727	0	1	1	1	2	2	2	2	3
58	1724	1721	1718	1715	1712	1709	1706	1704	1701	1698	0	1	1	1	1	2	2	2	3
59	1695	1692	1689	1686	1684	1681	1678	1675	1672	1669	0	1	1	1	1	2	2	2	3
60	1667	1664	1661	1658	1656	1653	1650	1647	1645	1642	0	1	1	1	1	2	2	2	3
61	1639	1637	1634	1631	1629	1626	1623	1621	1618	1616	0	1	1	1	1	2	2	2	2
62	1613	1610	1608	1605	1603	1600	1597	1595	1592	1590	0	1	1	1	1	2	2	2	2
63	1587	1585	1582	1580	1577	1575	1572	1570	1567	1565	0	0	1	1	1	1	2	2	2
64	1563	1560	1558	1555	1553	1550	1548	1546	1543	1541	0	0	1	1	1	1	2	2	2
65	1538	1536	1534	1531	1529	1527	1524	1522	1520	1517	0	0	1	1	1	1	2	2	2
66	1515	1513	1511	1508	1506	1504	1502	1499	1497	1495	0	0	1	1	1	1	2	2	2
67	1493	1490	1488	1486	1484	1481	1479	1477	1475	1473	0	0	1	1	1	1	2	2	2
68	1471	1468	1466	1464	1462	1460	1458	1456	1453	1451	0	0	1	1	1	1	2	2	2
69	1449	1447	1445	1443	1441	1439	1437	1435	1433	1431	0	0	1	1	1	1	1	2	2
70	1429	1427	1425	1422	1420	1418	1416	1414	1412	1410	0	0	1	1	1	1	1	2	2
71	1408	1406	1404	1403	1401	1399	1397	1395	1393	1391	0	0	1	1	1	1	1	2	2
72	1389	1387	1385	1383	1381	1379	1377	1376	1374	1372	0	0	1	1	1	1	1	2	2
73	1370	1368	1366	1364	1362	1361	1359	1357	1355	1353	0	0	1	1	1	1	1	2	2
74	1351	1350	1348	1346	1344	1342	1340	1339	1337	1335	0	0	1	1	1	1	1	1	2
75	1333	1332	1330	1328	1326	1325	1323	1321	1319	1318	0	0	1	1	1	1	1	1	2
76	1316	1314	1312	1311	1309	1307	1305	1304	1302	1300	0	0	1	1	1	1	1	1	2
77	1299	1297	1295	1294	1292	1290	1289	1287	1285	1284	0	0	0	1	1	1	1	1	1
78	1282	1280	1279	1277	1276	1274	1272	1271	1269	1267	0	0	0	1	1	1	1	1	1
79	1266	1264	1263	1261	1259	1258	1256	1255	1253	1252	0	0	0	1	1	1	1	1	1
80	1250	1248	1247	1245	1244	1242	1241	1239	1238	1236	0	0	0	1	1	1	1	1	1
81	1235	1233	1232	1230	1229	1227	1225	1224	1222	1221	0	0	0	1	1	1	1	1	1
82	1220	1218	1217	1215	1214	1212	1211	1209	1208	1206	0	0	0	1	1	1	1	1	1
83	1205	1203	1202	1200	1199	1198	1196	1195	1193	1192	0	0	0	1	1	1	1	1	1
84	1190	1189	1188	1186	1185	1183	1182	1181	1179	1178	0	0	0	1	1	1	1	1	1
85	1176	1175	1174	1172	1171	1170	1168	1167	1166	1164	0	0	0	1	1	1	1	1	1
86	1163	1161	1160	1159	1157	1156	1155	1153	1152	1151	0	0	0	1	1	1	1	1	1
87	1149	1148	1147	1145	1144	1143	1142	1140	1139	1138	0	0	0	1	1	1	1	1	1
88	1136	1135	1134	1133	1131	1130	1129	1127	1126	1125	0	0	0	1	1	1	1	1	1
89	1124	1122	1121	1120	1119	1117	1116	1115	1114	1112	0	0	0	1	1	1	1	1	1
90	1111	1110	1109	1107	1106	1105	1104	1103	1101	1100	0	0	0	1	1	1	1	1	1
91	1099	1098	1096	1095	1094	1093	1092	1091	1089	1088	0	0	0	1	1	1	1	1	1
92	1087	1086	1085	1083	1082	1081	1080	1079	1078	1076	0	0	0	0	1	1	1	1	1
93	1075	1074	1073	1072	1071	1070	1068	1067	1066	1065	0	0	0	1	1	1	1	1	1
94	1064	1063	1062	1060	1059	1058	1057	1056	1055	1054	0	0	0	1	1	1	1	1	1
95	1053	1052	1050	1049	1048	1047	1046	1045	1044	1043	0	0	0	1	1	1	1	1	1
96	1042	1041	1040	1038	1037	1036	1035	1034	1033	1032	0	0	0	1	1	1	1	1	1
97	1031	1030	1029	1028	1027	1026	1025	1024	1022	1021	0	0	0	1	1	1	1	1	1
98	1020	1019	1018	1017	1016	1015	1014	1013	1012	1011	0	0	0	1	1	1	1	1	1
99	1010	1009	1008	1007	1006	1005	1004	1003	1002	1001	0	0	0	0	1	1	1	1	1
	0	1	2	3	4	5	6	7	8	9	1	2	3	4	5	6	7	8	9
											Subtract Differences								

APPARATUS LIST

RECOMMENDED FOR THE THIRTY STARRED EXPERIMENTS WHICH ARE REGARDED AS FUNDAMENTAL

Numbers in parentheses refer to experiments.

Rectangular block of wood (2, 11, 57)
Rule, 30 cm. and 12 in. (2, 18, 57, 59)
Platform balance (Troemner model) with rider (2, 11, 12, 28, 30, 31)
(*Or*, Laboratory beam balance with rider)
Metric brass weights, 1 to 1000 grams, in block (2, 3, 4, 5, 6, 7, 11, 12, 28, 31)
Meter stick, Eng. and metric graduations (3, 4, 5, 6, 7, 28, 29, 54, 60)
Spool of black linen thread, No. 30 (3, 4, 11, 12)
Rider weight (lead) to fit meter stick (4)
Triangular wooden block (4)
Smooth board with rails and pulley for inclined plane (6, 7)
Hall's car (6)
Spring balance, 2000 grams and 64 oz. (3 required) (5, 6, 7, 18)
Pieces of marble, glass, sulfur (100–250 g.) (11)
Spring balance, 250 grams and 8 oz. (11)
Lead sinker with hook (11)
Battery jar, 6 × 8 in. (2 required) (11, 12)
Volumetric flask without stopper, 250 cm.³ (12)
Common salt, 1 lb. (12)
Hydrometer for light liquids (12)
Hydrometer for heavy liquids (12)
Towel, crash, 1 yd.², *or* paper, a roll (12)
Adjustable Boyle's-law apparatus, one tube (30 cm.³) graduated to 0.1 cm.³ and
provided with stopcock and pressure tubing, mounted on support rod (15)
Mercury, 1 lb. (15)
Mercurial barometer, Fortin cistern, with scale in in. and mm. (15, 28, 34)
Metric cross-section paper, note-book size (16)
Spiral (door) spring with weight hanger (17)
Table clamp for spring balance (3 required) (18)
Linen fishline (18)
Pencil compass (18)
Metric iron weights, slotted, 10 grams to 1000 grams, with holder (17, 22)
Ball, iron (about 0.75″ diam.) (21, 28)
Vernier caliper, metric, for inside, outside, and depth (21)
Linear expansion apparatus (lever form *or* Cowan's) (26)
Steam generator with support, including dipper and thermometer tube fitted
with a one-holed rubber stopper (26, 28, 30, 31, 34)
Bunsen burner (26, 29, 31, 34, 64) *or* electric heater *or* alcohol lamp
Rubber tubing, 0.25 in. for Bunsen burner, 3 ft. (26, 29, 31, 34, 64)
Thermometer, − 10° to 110° C., 12 in. long (26, 28, 30, 31, 32)
Cylindrical graduate, 200 cm.³ (28)
Calorimeter (double-walled with cover preferred) (28, 30, 31, 32)
Steam trap, large test tube with 2-holed stopper (31)
Rubber tubing, $\frac{3}{16}$ in., 3 ft. (31)

Sling psychrometer (32)

Bar magnets, cobalt-steel, 15 cm., pair (35)

Soft-iron washer, 2.2 cm. diam. (35)

Wood strips, 30 × 1 cm., pair (35)

Magnetic compass, 1 cm. (35)

Iron filings in carton with sifter top (35)

Voltmeter, triple range, D-C., 0–3, –15, –150 V., portable commercial type (36, 40, 41)

Simple voltaic cell, with jar, clamp, zinc, copper, carbon, and lead (36)

Sulfuric acid, 1 lb., c. p. (density 1.84) (36)

Copper wire, insulated, #20, 1 lb. (36)

Double connectors with set-screws (2 required) (36)

Dry cells (2 required), (36, 43, 46, 48)

Ammeter, double range, D-C., 0–3, –30 A., portable commercial type (37, 41)

Four coils A, 50 cm. #30 G.S.; B, 200 cm. #30; C, 200 cm. #27 G.S.; D, 2000 cm. #30 Copper wire (37)

Slide-wire bridge, Wheatstone, 1 meter (41)

Resistance box (dial form preferred) (41)

Storage battery, 3 cells, 6 volts (37, 40, 41)

Variable rheostat (12 ohm, 4 amp.) (40)

Knife-switch (40, 42)

Two coils wound with special resistance wire on porcelain tubes; 60 and 120 ohms for 110-volt line current, or 4 and 8 ohms for 6-volt battery current (40)

Magnetic compass, 2.5 cm. (35, 43, 48)

Soft-iron core, straight, 12.5 cm. long (42)

Soft-iron U-shaped core (42)

D'Arsonval galvanometer (41, 46, 48)

Induced-current coils about 600 turns of No. 28 wire (2 required) (46)

Magnet, U-shaped (46)

Dissectible " genamotor " (Cambosco) and electromagnetic field (47)

Rheostat, 10 ohms (47)

Tuning forks, C–256 and C'–512 frequencies (51)

Hydrometer jar, 2 × 12 in. (12, 51)

Glass resonance tube, 1.5 × 12 in. (51)

Photometer (Bunsen or Joly form) (54)

Two incandescent lamps, 25 and 50 watts (54)

Glass mirror, plane, 5 × 15 cm. (55)

Pins, ordinary, 0.5 lb. box (55, 56)

Box of rubber bands, assorted (29, 51)

Protractor (55, 59)

Convex-concave cylindrical mirror (metal) (56)

Glass refraction plate, rectangular (57)

Meter-stick supports for optical bench with lens holder, screen holder, and white screen, 10 cm. (58)

Double convex lens, 15 cm. focus, 3.8 cm. diam. (58)

Electric-lamp base to slide on meter stick (without lamp) (58)

Metal shield with wire-screen window to fit in front of lamp (58)

Log	0	1	2	3	4	5	6	7	8	9	1	2	3	4	5	6	7	8	9
.00	1000	1002	1005	1007	1009	1012	1014	1016	1019	1021	0	0	1	1	1	1	2	2	2
.01	1023	1026	1028	1030	1033	1035	1038	1040	1042	1045	0	0	1	1	1	1	2	2	2
.02	1047	1050	1052	1054	1057	1059	1062	1064	1067	1069	0	0	1	1	1	1	2	2	2
.03	1072	1074	1076	1079	1081	1084	1086	1089	1091	1094	0	0	1	1	1	1	2	2	2
.04	1096	1099	1102	1104	1107	1109	1112	1114	1117	1119	0	1	1	1	1	2	2	2	2
.05	1122	1125	1127	1130	1132	1135	1138	1140	1143	1146	0	1	1	1	1	2	2	2	2
.06	1148	1151	1153	1156	1159	1161	1164	1167	1169	1172	0	1	1	1	1	2	2	2	2
.07	1175	1178	1180	1183	1186	1189	1191	1194	1197	1199	0	1	1	1	1	2	2	2	2
.08	1202	1205	1208	1211	1213	1216	1219	1222	1225	1227	0	1	1	1	1	2	2	2	3
.09	1230	1233	1236	1239	1242	1245	1247	1250	1253	1256	0	1	1	1	1	2	2	2	3
.10	1259	1262	1265	1268	1271	1274	1276	1279	1282	1285	0	1	1	1	1	2	2	2	3
.11	1288	1291	1294	1297	1300	1303	1306	1309	1312	1315	0	1	1	1	2	2	2	2	3
.12	1318	1321	1324	1327	1330	1334	1337	1340	1343	1346	0	1	1	1	2	2	2	3	3
.13	1349	1352	1355	1358	1361	1365	1368	1371	1374	1377	0	1	1	1	2	2	2	3	3
.14	1380	1384	1387	1390	1393	1396	1400	1403	1406	1409	0	1	1	1	2	2	2	3	3
.15	1413	1416	1419	1422	1426	1429	1432	1435	1439	1442	0	1	1	1	2	2	2	3	3
.16	1445	1449	1452	1455	1459	1462	1466	1469	1472	1476	0	1	1	1	2	2	2	3	3
.17	1479	1483	1486	1489	1493	1496	1500	1503	1507	1510	0	1	1	1	2	2	2	3	3
.18	1514	1517	1521	1524	1528	1531	1535	1538	1542	1545	0	1	1	1	2	2	2	3	3
.19	1549	1552	1556	1560	1563	1567	1570	1574	1578	1581	0	1	1	1	2	2	3	3	3
.20	1585	1589	1592	1596	1600	1603	1607	1611	1614	1618	0	1	1	1	2	2	3	3	3
.21	1622	1626	1629	1633	1637	1641	1644	1648	1652	1656	0	1	1	2	2	2	3	3	3
.22	1660	1663	1667	1671	1675	1679	1683	1687	1690	1694	0	1	1	2	2	2	3	3	3
.23	1698	1702	1706	1710	1714	1718	1722	1726	1730	1734	0	1	1	2	2	2	3	3	4
.24	1738	1742	1746	1750	1754	1758	1762	1766	1770	1774	0	1	1	2	2	2	3	3	4
.25	1778	1782	1786	1791	1795	1799	1803	1807	1811	1816	0	1	1	2	2	2	3	3	4
.26	1820	1824	1828	1832	1837	1841	1845	1849	1854	1858	0	1	1	2	2	3	3	3	4
.27	1862	1866	1871	1875	1879	1884	1888	1892	1897	1901	0	1	1	2	2	3	3	3	4
.28	1905	1910	1914	1919	1923	1928	1932	1936	1941	1945	0	1	1	2	2	3	3	4	4
.29	1950	1954	1959	1963	1968	1972	1977	1982	1986	1991	0	1	1	2	2	3	3	4	4
.30	1995	2000	2004	2009	2014	2018	2023	2028	2032	2037	0	1	1	2	2	3	3	4	4
.31	2042	2046	2051	2056	2061	2065	2070	2075	2080	2084	0	1	1	2	2	3	3	4	4
.32	2089	2094	2099	2104	2109	2113	2118	2123	2128	2133	0	1	1	2	2	3	3	4	4
.33	2138	2143	2148	2153	2158	2163	2168	2173	2178	2183	0	1	1	2	2	3	3	4	4
.34	2188	2193	2198	2203	2208	2213	2218	2223	2228	2234	1	1	2	2	3	3	4	4	5
.35	2239	2244	2249	2254	2259	2265	2270	2275	2280	2286	1	1	2	2	3	3	4	4	5
.36	2291	2296	2301	2307	2312	2317	2323	2328	2333	2339	1	1	2	2	3	3	4	4	5
.37	2344	2350	2355	2360	2366	2371	2377	2382	2388	2393	1	1	2	2	3	3	4	4	5
.38	2399	2404	2410	2415	2421	2427	2432	2438	2443	2449	1	1	2	2	3	3	4	5	5
.39	2455	2460	2466	2472	2477	2483	2489	2495	2500	2506	1	1	2	2	3	3	4	5	5
.40	2512	2518	2523	2529	2535	2541	2547	2553	2559	2564	1	1	2	2	3	4	4	5	5
.41	2570	2576	2582	2588	2594	2600	2606	2612	2618	2624	1	1	2	2	3	4	4	5	5
.42	2630	2636	2642	2649	2655	2661	2667	2673	2679	2685	1	1	2	2	3	4	4	5	6
.43	2692	2698	2704	2710	2716	2723	2729	2735	2742	2748	1	1	2	3	3	4	4	5	6
.44	2754	2761	2767	2773	2780	2786	2793	2799	2805	2812	1	1	2	3	3	4	4	5	6
.45	2818	2825	2831	2838	2844	2851	2858	2864	2871	2877	1	1	2	3	3	4	5	5	6
.46	2884	2891	2897	2904	2911	2917	2924	2931	2938	2944	1	1	2	3	3	4	5	5	6
.47	2951	2958	2965	2972	2979	2985	2992	2999	3006	3013	1	1	2	3	3	4	5	5	6
.48	3020	3027	3034	3041	3048	3055	3062	3069	3076	3083	1	1	2	3	4	4	5	6	6
.49	3090	3097	3105	3112	3119	3126	3133	3141	3148	3155	1	1	2	3	4	4	5	6	6
	0	1	2	3	4	5	6	7	8	9	1	2	3	4	5	6	7	8	9